DO YOUR OWN
CENTRAL HEATING
INSTALLATION

DO YOUR OWN

CENTRAL HEATING INSTALLATION

TREVOR CRABTREE
C. Eng. M.I.Prod.E.

Edited by
RON GRACE

Do-it-Yourself Magazine

London
W. FOULSHAM & CO LTD
New York · Toronto · Capetown · Sydney

W. FOULSHAM & CO LTD
Yeovil Road, Slough, Berks, England

PHOTOGRAPHS OF PRODUCTS BY THE FOLLOWING
COMPANIES HAVE BEEN USED:

Baxi Heating,
Bamber Bridge, Preston, PR5 6SN
Damixa Ltd.,
Reynard Mills Trading Estate, Windmill Road,
Brentford, Middlesex, TW8 9NG
Drayton Controls (Engineering) Ltd.,
West Drayton, Middlesex, UB7 8JW
Dunsley Heating Appliance Co. Ltd.,
Fearnought, Huddersfield Road, Holmfirth, Nr. Huddersfield, HD7 2TU
Honeywell Ltd.,
Charles Square, Bracknell, Berks, RG12 1EB
Myson Group Marketing Ltd.,
Industrial Estate, Ongar, Essex, CM5 9RE
Potterton International Ltd.,
Portobello Works, Emscote Road, Warwick, CV34 5QU
Stelrad Group Ltd.,
P.O. Box 103, National Avenue, Hull, HU5 4JN
Trianco Redfyre Ltd.,
Stewart House, Brook Way, Kingston Road,
Leatherhead, Surrey, KT22 7LY

ISBN 0-572-01054-0

Printed and bound in Great Britain
at The Bath Press, Avon

CONTENTS

FOREWORD

As far back as Roman times, private houses were being built in Britain which were designed to be heated from a central fireplace. Although primitive, this is considered to be the origin of central heating in this country.

Due probably to the limitations of plumbing, heating systems as we know them today did not come into use until many years later. Even then, they were mainly confined to large buildings such as assembly halls and schools. Such systems were exclusively of the piped variety. That is, they operated by the movement of hot water through pipework and radiators. In some cases, steam was used instead of hot water.

The modern domestic piped central heating system is purely a scaled down and simplified version of the former large type of installation. Modern technology and fuels have brought about certain changes, but the principles remain.

Because modern materials are easy to work and handle, the installation of most domestic piped central heating systems is now within the scope of the average handyman. The only other requirement on the part of the installer is the willingness to undertake a certain amount of planning and hard work.

This book has been written with the object of describing and comparing the various types of domestic piped central heating systems, and the method of designing and installing them. An attempt has been made to deal fully with each item of equipment under separate headings which may easily be found for reference.

This book deals only with piped systems, although various other types are available. The piped method is generally considered to be one of the most expensive to install, but the cheapest to run. It therefore makes best economic sense, apart from increasing the value of the building. Other methods may well prove to be the opposite as far as installation and running costs are concerned.

By supplying the labour himself, the d-i-y installer can now take advantage of having a piped system which has cost little more than the materials.

I
BUILDING CONSTRUCTION AND TEMPERATURE

Every building is different. Methods and materials from which they are constructed vary. Some are better insulated than others, and the people occupying them have different requirements. These, and other factors, must all be considered when setting out to design a heating system.

HEAT TRANSMITTANCE

Any material used for a building will allow heat to pass through itself to a certain extent. During cold weather, this causes heat to be lost from the inside to the outside. The greater the temperature difference from inside to outside, the greater will be the heat loss. For room temperatures to be maintained, the heating system must be capable of delivering at least as much heat to the rooms as is being lost to the outside.

HEAT MEASUREMENT

Heat is measured in British Thermal Units (B.Th.Us.), and one B.Th.U. is the amount of heat required to raise the temperature of one pound of water by 1°F. One gallon of water weighs ten pounds and, therefore, ten B.Th.Us. will be required to raise its temperature from, say, 59°F to 60°F. If the same gallon of water is now allowed to cool back to 59°F, it will give out ten B.Th.Us. of heat.

AREA AND VOLUME OF ROOMS

In order to calculate heat losses, the area of each part of the house in question needs to be known, as must also be the volume of each room. This calls only for simple measurement and arithmetic, but consider the structure shown in Fig. 1.

Because the areas of the door and window need also to be known, time will be saved by proceeding as follows:
Area of door is $2 \cdot 5 \times 6 \cdot 5 = 16.25$ sq. ft.
Area of window is $6 \times 3 = 18$ sq. ft.
Area of wall is total area — area of door — area of window.
$$= (15 \times 9) - 16 \cdot 25 - 18$$
$$= 135 - 16 \cdot 25 - 18$$
$$= 100 \cdot 75 \text{ sq. ft.}$$

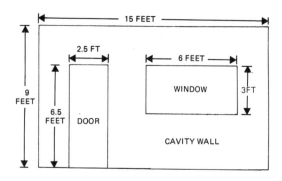

Fig. 1   Dimensions of one section of a building.

HEAT TRANSMITTANCE COEFFICIENT (U-VALUE)

The ease with which heat is able to pass through any material is known as the heat transmittance coefficient, or U-value, of that material. Depending on how exposed a building may be, the U-values may be expected to vary slightly, and those given below are average figures. All values are quoted in B.Th.Us. per square foot per hour per °F temperature difference, and worked examples can be found in this, and the next chapter.

	U-value (B.Th.Us./ sq.ft./hr./°F)
EXTERNAL WALLS	
Brickwork, plastered inside.	
9 in. solid	0·42
11 in. ventilated cavity	0.34
11 in. unventilated cavity	0·3
INTERNAL WALLS	
4½ in. brick, plastered both sides	0·44
4½ in. breeze block, plastered both sides	0·4
4½ in. dry partition, plastered both sides	0·3
DOORS	
All types	0·5
WINDOWS	
Single glazed	1·0
Double glazed	0·5
FLAT ROOFS	
Asphalt on 6 in. thick concrete, plastered	0·55

Asphalt on 6 in. thick concrete with 2 in. thick cork, plastered	0·12

PITCHED ROOFS

Plaster ceiling with tiles on battens	0·58
Plaster ceiling with tiles on battens, with 3 in. glass fibre insulation	0·16
Plaster ceiling with felt and tiles on battens	0.43
Plaster ceiling with felt and tiles on battens, with 3 in. glass fibre insulation	0·10

FLOORS

Ground, with wooden boards on joists	0·28
Ground, solid	0·18
Intermediate, plaster ceiling with wooden floorboards on joists	0·28

WOOD

Tongued and grooved

1 in. thick	0·48
1½ in. thick	0·39

SYSTEM TEMPERATURES

Consideration must also be given as to what the individual room temperatures are to be. This is purely a matter of personal choice, but the generally accepted figures are:

Living rooms, bathrooms	70°F
Halls, landings, kitchens	65°F
Bedrooms	60°F

An assumption must also be made as to what the outside temperature will be. This is normally taken to be 30°F, and ensures that the system will be able to attain the required temperatures when there is 2°F of frost outside.

For semi-detached properties, an assumption is also made for the temperature on the far side of party walls. This is usually taken to be 55°F downstairs, and 50°F for bedrooms and landing. A wall adjoining an entry or garage counts as an outside wall.

HEAT LOSS

A calculation can now be made of the amount of heat passing through any wall, ceiling or floor of a building. Suppose that for the section shown in Fig. 1, the brickwork is 11 in. thick with a ventilated cavity, and the window is single glazed. The inside temperature is 65°F, and the outside, 30°F.

Then, heat loss through the structure is the area times the U-value, times the temperature difference in degrees F.

For door, loss is $16 \cdot 25 \times 0 \cdot 5 \times 35 = 284 \cdot 38$

For window, loss is $18 \times 1 \cdot 0 \times 35 = 630$

For wall, loss is $100 \cdot 75 \times 0 \cdot 34 \times 35 = 1,198 \cdot 93$

Therefore the loss through the structure is   2,113·31 B.Th.Us. per hour.

In cases where a warm room adjoins a cooler one, heat will pass through the wall from the warmer to the cooler. The cooler room will thus gain heat through that wall. For this reason, the calculations in the next chapter have separate loss and gain columns. The heat gained is subtracted from that lost, and the heating system is required only to make up the remaining amount.

If in doubt as to the actual construction of any part of a building, always select the higher U-value to give the worst condition. It is also sometimes necessary to modify the value used. For example, the figure given for doors of all types is $0 \cdot 5$, and that for single glazed windows is $1 \cdot 0$. For a door containing a large area of single glass, a U-value of $1 \cdot 0$ would be more accurate.

AIR CHANGES

The air in a building is never static. Even closed doors and windows have cracks around them, and these are sufficient to allow air to pass into the building, around and out again. Because it has been warmed, the air as it leaves takes a certain amount of heat with it, and this is replaced by air from the outside which is cold. This heat loss due to air changes must be made good.

It is again necessary to make an assumption as to the number of air changes which occur, and the generally accepted figures are:

Living rooms, bedrooms, 1½ changes per hour.

Others, 2 changes per hour.

By reference to the basic definition of the B.Th.U., it can be shown that the heat required to raise the temperature of one cubic foot of air by 1°F is 0·02 B.Th.Us. The resulting heat loss can now be calculated.

Suppose that a living room contains 2,250 cubic feet of air which is at 70°F. The outside temperature is 30°F. Then, heat loss due to air changes is the volume times 0·02 times the number of changes per hour times the temperature difference in degrees F.

$= 2{,}250 \times 0{\cdot}02 \times 1{\cdot}5 \times 40$
$= 2{,}700$ B.Th.Us. per hour.

This must be added to the loss through the walls, ceiling and floor.

It should be noted that, in carrying out these calculations, all room sizes are given in feet, or decimals of a foot. The following conversion table may be found useful:

 1 inch is equal to 0·08 of a foot
 2 inches is equal to 0·17 of a foot
 3 inches is equal to 0·25 of a foot
 4 inches is equal to 0·33 of a foot
 5 inches is equal to 0·42 of a foot
 6 inches is equal ot 0·5 of a foot
 7 inches is equal to 0·58 of a foot
 8 inches is equal to 0·67 of a foot
 9 inches is equal to 0·75 of a foot
 10 inches is equal to 0·83 of a foot
 11 inches is equal to 0·92 of a foot

INSULATION

By inspection of the U-values quoted, the heat saving effects of insulation can be seen. for example, the heat loss through a window can be halved by double glazing, but that will not, of course, halve the total loss from the room.

For the window in the structure shown in Fig. 1, the calculation becomes:

For door, loss is $16{\cdot}25 \times 0{\cdot}5 \times 35 \;=\; 284{\cdot}38$
For window, loss is $18 \times 0{\cdot}5 \times 35 \;=\; 315$
For wall, loss is $100{\cdot}75 \times 0{\cdot}34 \times 35 = 1{,}198{\cdot}93$

Therefore the loss through the $1{,}798{\cdot}31$ B.Th.Us.
structure is   per hour.

Generally speaking, the greatest heat saving will be obtained by improving the insulation in parts of a building which are:

 1. Of large area.
 2. Of high temperature difference with the sur-
   roundings.

This means that windows, outside walls and roofs are the most suitable places for attention.

2
HEAT REQUIREMENTS

HEAT LOSS FROM ROOMS

It is now possible, using certain assumptions stated previously, to find the total heat loss for any building. Two items will greatly assist in making these calculations.

1. A drawing of each floor of the building, preferably to scale. It sould be drawn as large as possible, and have marked on it:

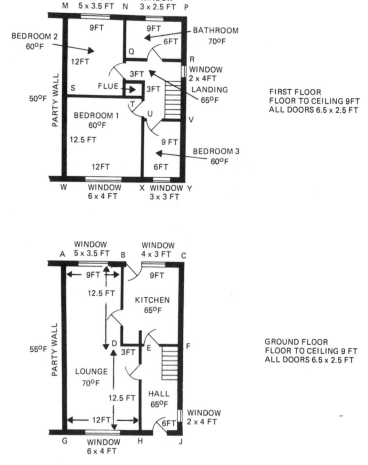

Fig. 2   Plan of a typical semi-detached two-storey house.

(i) The sizes of rooms, windows and doors in feet.

(ii) The required temperature in each area, including the assumed temperature in adjoining properties.

(iii) An arbitrary letter at each wall junction.

If a copying machine is available, it is a good idea to prepare the drawing on a master sheet. This can then be reproduced as necessary, and may be used for further stages of the design work. The drawing is shown in Fig. 2.

2. An electronic calculator. Even the simplest type will be sufficient for the work involved.

Each room is then dealt with in turn, as follows:

LOUNGE AREAS are:

For AB, window is 5×3.5	=	17·5 sq. ft.
wall is $(9 \times 9) - 17.5$	=	63·5 sq. ft.
For BD, door is 6.5×2.5	=	16·25 sq. ft.
wall is $(12.5 \times 9) - 16.25$	=	96·25 sq. ft.
For DE, wall is 3×9	=	27 sq. ft.
For EH, door is 6.5×2.5	=	16·25 sq. ft.
wall is $(12.5 \times 9) - 16.25$	=	96·25 sq. ft.
For GH, window is 6×4	=	24 sq. ft.
wall is $(12 \times 9) - 24$	=	84 sq. ft.
For AG, wall is 25×9	=	225 sq. ft.
Floor is $(12.5 \times 9) + (12.5 \times 12)$	=	262·5 sq. ft.
Ceiling is $(12.5 \times 9) + (12.5 \times 12)$	=	262·5 sq. ft.

LOUNGE VOLUME is 262.5×9 = 2,362·5 cu. ft.

LOUNGE HEAT CHANGES are:

		Loss	Gain
For AB, window is $17.5 \times 1.0 \times 40$	=	700	
wall is $63.5 \times 0.34 \times 40$	=	863·6	
For BD, door is $16.25 \times 0.5 \times 5$	=	40·63	
wall is $96.25 \times 0.4 \times 5$	=	192·5	
For DE, wall is $27 \times 0.4 \times 5$	=	54	
For EH, door is $16.25 \times 0.5 \times 5$	=	40·63	
wall is $96.25 \times 0.4 \times 5$	=	192·5	
For GH, window is $24 \times 1.0 \times 40$	=	960	
wall is $84 \times 0.34 \times 40$	=	1,142·4	
For AG, wall is $225 \times 0.34 \times 15$	=	1,147·5	
Floor is $262.5 \times 0.28 \times 40$	=	2,940	
Ceiling is $262.5 \times 0.28 \times 10$	=	735	
Air change is $2,362.5 \times 0.02 \times 1.5 \times 40$ =		2,835	
		11,843·76	Nil

Then, LOUNGE HEAT LOSS is losses − gains
$$= 11{,}843{\cdot}76 - 0$$
$$= 11{,}843{\cdot}76$$
$$= 11{,}844 \text{ B.Th.Us. per hour (rounded)}$$

KITCHEN AREAS are:

For BC, door is 6·5 × 2·5	=	16·25 sq. ft.
window is 4 × 3	=	12 sq. ft.
wall is (9 × 9) − 16·25 − 12	=	52·75 sq. ft.
For CF, wall is 12 × 9	=	108 sq. ft.
For EF, door is 6·5 × 2·5	=	16·25 sq. ft.
wall is (6 × 9) − 16·25	=	37·75 sq. ft.
For DE, wall is 2·5 × 9	=	22·5 sq. ft.
For BD, door is 6·5 × 2·5	=	16·25 sq. ft.
wall is (12 × 9) − 16·25	=	91·75 sq. ft.
Floor is 12 × 9	=	108 sq. ft.
Ceiling is 12 × 9	=	108 sq. ft.

KITCHEN VOLUME is 108 × 9   =   972 cu. ft.

KITCHEN HEAT CHANGES are:	Loss	Gain
For BC, door is 16·25 × 0·5 × 35 =	284·38	
window is 12 × 1·0 × 35 =	420	
wall is 52·75 × 0·34 × 35 =	627·73	
For CF, wall is 108 × 0·34 × 35 =	1,285·2	
For EF, no temperature difference =	Nil	= Nil
For DE, wall is 22·5 × 0·4 × 5		= 45
For BD, door is 16·25 × 0·5 × 5		= 40·63
wall is 91·75 × 0·4 × 5		=183·5
Floor is 108 × 0·18 × 35 =	680·4	
Ceiling is (6 ÷ 12) × 108 × 0·28 × 5		= 75·6
Air change is 975 × 0·02 × 2 × 35 =	1,360·8	
	4,658·51	344·73

Then, KITCHEN HEAT LOSS is losses − gains
$$= 4{,}658{\cdot}51 - 344{\cdot}73$$
$$= 4{,}313{\cdot}78$$
$$= 4{,}314 \text{ B.Th.Us. per hour (rounded)}$$

The calculations for the heat losses in the remaining rooms are carried out exactly as shown above. In the case of the hall, landing and stairs, the loss at each level can be calculated separately, and the two added together.

Because the heat loss from each room must be made good by the heating system, the calculations show the output required from the radiators or other heating units. If, for example, the lounge is to be heated by radiators alone, these must be sized such that an output of at least 11,844 B.Th.Us. per hour can be achieved.

Before the total required output from the boiler can be determined, there are two further aspects which must be considered.

DOMESTIC HOT WATER

In systems where the domestic hot water is also to be supplied from the heating system, this must be allowed for when calculating the output of the boiler.

The size of the family will largely dictate the capacity of the hot water storage cylinder. Thirty gallons is adequate in most cases, but this may be increased when the demand for hot water is expected to be high. Generally speaking, a shower requires less hot water than a bath.

A decision must also be made as to roughly what the required temperature of the hot water is to be. 130°F is a reasonable figure, and it is usual to assume that the water in the cylinder will take three hours to reach this level.

A calculation of the amount of heat which must be supplied by the boiler to heat the domestic water can now be made. Suppose that the capacity of the cylinder is 30 gallons, and that a water temperature of 130°F is required. A reheat time of three hours can be allowed.

Then, one gallon of water weighs ten pounds
Therefore the weight of water in cylinder is 30 × 10
$$= 300 \text{ pounds}$$
Temperature rise is 130°F − 30°F = 100°F.
Therefore the heat required is 300 × 100
$$= 30,000 \text{ B.Th.Us. total.}$$
For a reheat time of three hours, heat required per hour is
$$30,000 \div 3$$
$$= 10,000 \text{ B.Th.Us. per hour.}$$

It should be noted that the three-hour reheat period will apply only when the central heating system is in operation, and the outside temperature is 30°F.

BOILER ALLOWANCE

In the calculations so far, the outside temperature has been assumed to be 30°F. On certain occasions, of course, it falls lower than this. To cover such an event, it is usual to increase the size, and thus, the heat output of the boiler, by a certain amount. This is known as the boiler allowance, or boiler margin.

The allowances normally applied are:

    Solid fuel boilers 15% to 25%
    Oil and gas boilers 10% to 15%

Where boilers are intermittently operated, for example, by time switches, the higher percentage should be used. The lower figure will suffice in other cases.

The allowance is applied after accounting for all other heat requirements, as is shown later in this chapter.

TOTAL BOILER OUTPUT

It is now possible to arrive at the total boiler output required. For the example shown in Fig. 2, this would be:

Lounge	11,844
Kitchen	4,314
Hall, landing and stairs	6,381
Bedroom 1	4,402
Bedroom 2	3,065
Bedroom 3	2,435
Bathroom	4,062
Hot water (30 gallons, three hour reheat)	10,000
	————
Therefore the total heating load is	46,503
15% allowance (gas boiler, intermittent)	6,975
	————
	53,478 B.Th.Us. per hr.

It can thus be seen that a boiler which gives an output of about 53,500 B.Th.Us. per hour should be chosen for this installation. If a much larger boiler is used, it will merely switch itself on and off too frequently. On the other hand, too small a boiler will not be able to maintain the room and hot water temperatures required during freezing conditions.

3
DOMESTIC HOT WATER AND CENTRAL HEATING SYSTEMS

By far the majority of heating systems being installed today are of the piped variety. That is, they operate by heating water in a central boiler, the water then being pumped around the building inside pipes. The pipes carry the water to radiators and heat exchangers, which allow the water partially to cool and thus give off heat to warm the rooms. The water then returns to the boiler to be reheated and circulated again.

In dwelling houses, it is usual to arrange the system so that the domestic hot water is also heated by the boiler. To obtain hot water during warmer weather, the boiler is still used, but the heating system is switched off so that the radiators remain cold.

SMALL BORE SYSTEMS

This is the most common type, and uses pipework of 15mm., 22mm. and, sometimes, 28mm. diameter to feed the radiators. In some cases, pipework of up to 35mm. diameter is used in the domestic hot water part of the system. This is usually confined to the two pipes connecting the boiler to the hot water cylinder.

A typical small bore domestic hot water and central heating system is shown in Fig. 3. It should be noted that two header tanks are required. The larger one is for the domestic water, as in any hot water system. The smaller one, known as the feed and expansion tank, is for the central heating, and serves two purposes:

1. To replenish any water loss from the system.
2. To absorb any volume expansion of the water caused by heating.

Each tank is fed with water from the mains, the levels being controlled by ball valves. Each tank must also be fitted with a suitable overflow pipe. To aid clarity, the mains feeds and overflows are not shown on the diagrams in this book.

In the system shown, a control valve is required. In warm weather when the heating is not needed, this is closed. The boiler is thus able to heat the domestic water, but not the radiators. Such valves may be turned by hand, but motorised valves operated by electricity are more usual. These are described more fully in Chapter 13 (page 92).

17

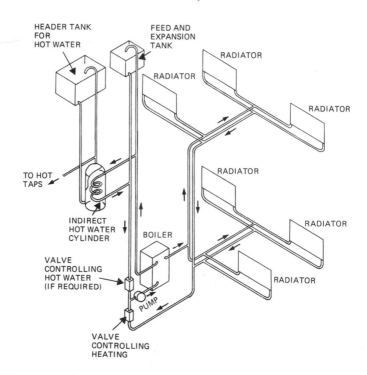

Fig. 3   Small bore domestic hot water and central heating system.

A second valve, to control the temperature of the hot water, is shown. If temperature control of the hot water is not required, this valve is omitted. This, again, is described more fully in Chapter 13.

MICROBORE SYSTEMS

In recent years, microbore systems have entered the central heating field. These use the much smaller pipe sizes of 6mm., 8mm. and 10mm. diameter for certain parts. Because these pipes are of such small size, the friction set up against the water flow is raised, and pipe length becomes much more important than with small bore systems.

Microbore systems may be split into two distinct types.

1. Those based on a small bore type circulation, similar to that shown in Fig. 3, but with certain pipe sizes being reduced. This method is not suitable for every building.

18

2. Those using devices known as manifolds, as shown in Fig. 4. The manifolds, usually one for each storey, are fed by small bore pipework from the boiler. They distribute the water to each radiator using microbore pipework. After passing through a radiator, the water returns to the manifold via micro-bore pipes. The manifold collects this cooled water and returns it to the boiler inside small bore pipes.

The main disadvantage of the manifold method is that, in many cases, the total length of pipe required is increased.

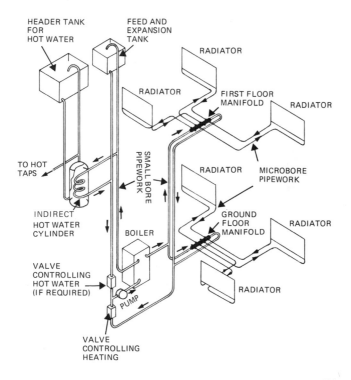

Fig. 4   Domestic hot water and central heating system, using small bore and microbore pipework with manifolds.

The system shown in Fig 4 uses small bore pipework between the boiler and hot water cylinder. It is possible to use microbore pipe for this, but the system must be modi-fied slightly, as shown in Fig. 5.

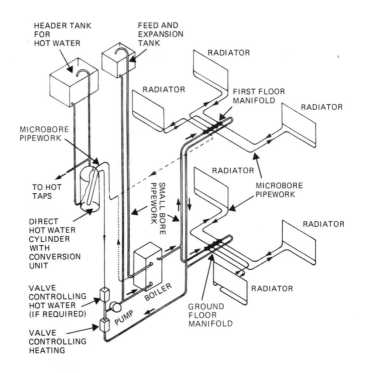

HEADER TANK FOR HOT WATER

FEED AND EXPANSION TANK

RADIATOR

RADIATOR

FIRST FLOOR MANIFOLD

RADIATOR

MICROBORE PIPEWORK

SMALL BORE PIPEWORK

TO HOT TAPS

RADIATOR

MICROBORE PIPEWORK

DIRECT HOT WATER CYLINDER WITH CONVERSION UNIT

RADIATOR

VALVE CONTROLLING HOT WATER (IF REQUIRED)

BOILER

RADIATOR

GROUND FLOOR MANIFOLD

VALVE CONTROLLING HEATING

PUMP

Fig. 5   Domestic hot water and central heating system, using microbore feed to the hot water cylinder.

Because the feed and expansion tank needs to be connected with small bore pipes, these are joined directly into the boiler.

The feed to the hot water cylinder may follow one of two routes:

1. Directly from the boiler, as shown by the dotted line.
2. From the upstairs manifold, as shown by the broken line.

SEALED SYSTEMS

There are two reasons for considering a sealed system:

1. For installation into buildings where the header tanks cannot be at a sufficient height, for example, in flats. Such systems can be operated at normal temperatures.
2. For systems which are required to operate above the boiling point of water. At normal atmospheric

pressure, water boils at 212°F, and an open heating system should not be operated at above 180°F. In a sealed system, the pressure can be set at some level above atmospheric, and operating temperatures of up to 220°F can be used without the water boiling. It is no longer possible to use radiators or exposed pipework, due to the danger of burning. Fan convectors or skirting heaters are the only types of heating unit which can be used with safety, as neither of these have exposed parts which are at water temperature.

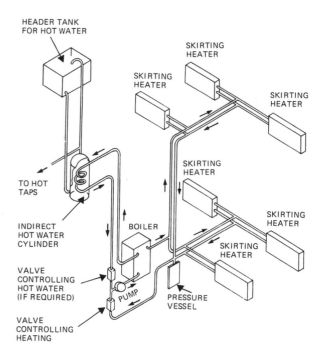

Fig. 6   Sealed domestic hot water and central heating system, using small bore pipework.

A small bore sealed system is shown in Fig. 6. Either small bore or microbore pipework, with or without manifolds, can be used.

It should be noted that only one header tank, for the domestic water, is now required. Where height is restricted, a position just below ceiling level is usually adequate for this. Expansion of the volume of water contained in the system is absorbed by the pressure vessel, and this is explained more fully in Chapter 10.

A sealed system, provided that it is properly designed, maintained and operated, is as safe as an open one. Leakage of water from any part cannot be allowed, as this leads to a pressure drop with a consequent fall in the temperature at which the water will boil. Safety devices are of the utmost importance.

It is also necessary, when designing and installing a sealed system, to ensure that all items are suitable for the use to which they will be put. Specifications must be checked to see that the elevated temperatures and pressures encountered can be withstood.

Some water boards do not allow the connection of sealed systems directly to their pipework, and this point must be clarified before proceeding with this type of installation. Property insurance, too, sometimes covers only open heating systems.

4
BOILERS AND FLUES

The boiler may be regarded as the heart of any heating system. The calculations in Chapters 1 and 2 show the method used to determine the heat output required. Serious consideration must now be given to the type of fuel to be used. This will not only have a bearing on the installation and running costs, but can also dictate the design and operation of the system itself.

With regard to fuel costs, comparisons between types are difficult because that which appears to be cheapest now may well turn out to be the most expensive in five years' time. Means by which running costs can be reduced are:

1. By insulating the building, and keeping outside doors closed as much as possible.
2. By ensuring that excessively high room temperatures are not reached.
3. By not running the system when everyone is out. Time switches can be used so that the rooms are warm when people arrive home (but solid fuel boilers are less controllable than others).
4. By buying fuel on the most suitable tariff.

SOLID FUEL

The burning of a solid fuel, that is wood or coal, is the oldest method by which man has warmed himself. Modern technology has resulted in great changes both to the fuel itself, and the way that it is handled and used. Some things have not changed – the fuel is still burned, resulting in an ash which must be periodically removed.

The modern boiler falls into one of two types:

1. Room heaters. These fit into a fireplace and have a back boiler to provide heat for the domestic hot water and central heating. Radiant heat is passed to the room via a glass fronted door, and some models also have convector grilles.

    Stoking is usually carried out directly by opening the door, but some models have a hopper. The contents of this are gravity fed to the fire as required.

    Burning rate is controlled by a thermostatic damper.
2. Free standing. These are designed for the purpose of providing hot water for domestic and heating use,

Dunsley open fire with back boiler, installed in a living room.

and may be regarded purely as boilers. Hopper fed types are again available.

The usual method of control of the burning rate is by thermostatic damper. However, some models are fitted with an electric fan which gives a faster warm-up and better control.

Solid fuel boilers cannot be switched off quickly, as is the case with oil and gas fired types. Neither is it possible to control the temperature of the water within close limits. Because of this, the pipework system must be designed so that a flow of water through the boiler is always possible, and the methods of achieving this are explained fully in Chapter 12.

It should be noted that any solid fuel boiler requires a certain amount of fuel to attain any required temperature. Correct stoking and damper setting are thus required if acceptable operation is to be achieved, and this means that far more attention is required by the user than with other methods of firing.

Dunsley flued back boiler unit.

OIL

For domestic purposes, there are several different methods by which oil can be burned to produce heat. These methods, in turn, use oil of two different viscosities, or thicknesses – 28 second and 35 second. Of these, the heavier 35 second grade is currently cheaper by a small margin.

Boiler types consist of:

1. Pressure jet, using 35 second oil. these employ a pump which forces the oil through a small jet at a pressure of about 100 pounds per square inch. A fan is used to supply the amount of air required, and ignition of the oil takes place by means of a device resembling a motor car spark plug. The size of the jet determines the boiler output, and this can be changed easily, within a certain range, if required.

Trianco Redfyre Housemaster De Luxe, anthracite gravity feed hearth boiler.

Generally, these boilers are too noisy to be installed in a kitchen, and a separate boiler house is required.
2. Down firing pressure jet, using either 35 second or 28 second oil. These are recent developments of pressure jet boilers, and may be installed either in a boiler house, burning 35 second oil, or in a kitchen, where 28 second oil is used.
3. Wallflame, using 28 second oil. The principle of this type can be seen by reference to Fig. 7.
The oil is fed via a control valve to a distributor, which is driven by an electric motor. The distributor sprays oil outwards to the flame rim, where it ignites and burns, thus heating the inside of the surrounding water jacket. The motor also powers a fan which supplies a draught to assist combustion. When starting up, the oil is ignited by electrical means, but

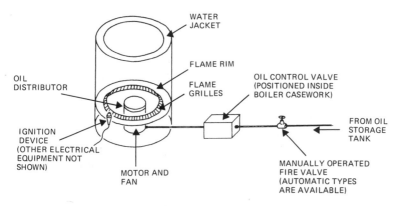

Fig. 7 *Wallflame type oil boiler.*

Trianco Redfyre Centramatic oil-fired boiler, with balanced flue.

Trianco Redfyre TRO oil-fired boiler, with conventional flue.

after a short time, the flame grilles become sufficiently hot to cause the oil to burn.

Wallflame boilers are suitable for installation in kitchens, and are probably the most popular type. They are by no means silent in operation, but their noise level, on the other hand, is likely to prove acceptable.

4. Dynaflame, using 35 second or 28 second oil. These are similar to wallflame boilers, but employ a slightly different method of combustion. They are suitable either for kitchen use (28 second oil), or for installation in a boiler house (35 second oil).

Unlike solid fuel types, these boilers are completely automatic in operation, and can be started up or shut down using electrical time switches. In the event of a burner not igniting correctly, a unit known as a flame failure device operates. This switches the boiler off and prevents any leakage of unburned oil.

Water temperature control is achieved by a thermostat positioned inside the water jacket, and this switches the burners on or off as required. A constant flow of water through the boiler is not necessary, and a greater choice of pipework arrangements is thus possible.

OIL STORAGE

A tank to contain the fuel oil is required, and this is usually arranged to give a gravity feed to the boiler. It is

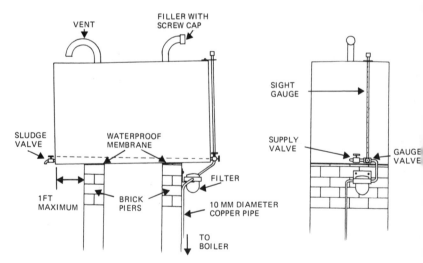

Fig. 8   Arrangement of oil storage tank and equipment.

normal for the price per gallon of oil to decrease as the number of gallons delivered increases, and for better economy, a minimum tank capacity of 600 gallons should be installed. This will allow deliveries of 500 gallons to be made at one time.

It is important that the tank is strongly supported, as when full, a 600 gallon tank weighs about three tons. A typical arrangement is shown in Fig. 8.

Several aspects should be noted:

1. Two brick piers are shown, but more may be necessary to support the weight. These must be built on strong foundations, and have a waterproof membrane (thick polythene will suffice) between them and the tank bottom.

2. The tank should slope slightly downwards, and be fitted with a sludge valve. This is to prevent water from condensation, and rust, from entering the supply pipe. The valve should be opened periodically and the sludge drained off.

3. A vent is required at the top of the tank, which is designed so that rain cannot enter. The diameter of the vent pipe should be at least equal to that of the filler pipe.

4. A filler pipe with a screw cap should be fitted as near as possible to the highest point on the tank. The thread of the filler must be $1\frac{1}{2}$ or 2in. size to match the equipment normally carried by delivery tankers.

5. An accurate contents gauge is required, and a simple sight type is shown in Fig. 8. This may be made from semi-transparent nylon pipe, and fitted with a valve which is opened to take a reading. Dial type contents gauges are not so accurate, and the internal mechanism of some models will rust, causing them to jam. These should be avoided, as any oil which overflows when the tank is being filled has to be paid for.

6. A filter must be fitted to remove any dirt which would otherwise enter the supply pipe. These are usually of the glass bowl type, and should be cleaned out periodically.

7. A supply valve should be fitted so that the oil flow can be stopped for filter cleaning.

8. The tank is connected to the boiler using 10mm. diameter copper pipe, and this can be up to 60ft. long. A fire valve is fitted near to the boiler, and this is shown in Fig. 7.

Most boilers require the tank top and fuel outlet to be within certain specified limits above the oil control valve. The installation instructions for the boiler must be consulted in order that these requirements are met.

GAS

Unlike solid fuel and oil, a gas supply is not dependent on road deliveries, neither is space required for fuel storage. In operation, the only audible sound is a hiss, and thus installation in a boiler house is not required for noise reduction purposes.

There are several different types:

1. Combined boilers and fires. These are boilers which are designed to be fitted into a fireplace opening, and supply hot water for domestic and central heating purposes. A separate gas fire is fitted in front of the boiler to heat the room. The boiler and fire are quite independent of each other, and are controlled separately.

2. Free-standing. This is the well known type of gas boiler, often installed in a kitchen, which is used to supply both the domestic hot water and central heat-

Baxi Bermuda LFE combined boiler and gas fire, with 'glowing coals' effect.

ing. Most models are capable of being set to give a particular heat output within a specified range, and this is achieved by regulation of the gas pressure. A typical gas burner is shown in Fig. 9, and ignition may be either electrical, or by a constantly burning pilot flame.

3. Wall mounted. These are a fairly recent development, and, as the name suggests, are designed to be mounted on a wall. They are relatively small in size, and may even be installed inside a cupboard.

As a result of their small size, they contain far less water than other types of boiler. This gives a rapid warm-up, but also means that the water must be passed through the unit rapidly, otherwise local overheating can occur. Special pipework and control systems are sometimes required, and these are shown in Chapters 12 and 13.

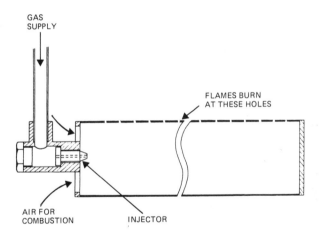

Fig. 9   A typical gas burner.

Like oil boilers, gas models are completely automatic in operation. Flame failure devices are fitted to cut off the supply of gas in the event of the ignition system not operating correctly.

CONVENTIONAL AND BALANCED FLUES

In the past, boilers were designed for use with conventional flues and Fig. 10 shows a free-standing boiler discharging via a cast iron pipe into a brick flue.

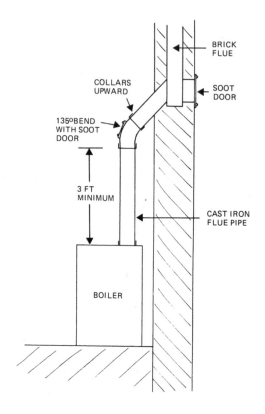

Fig. 10   Free standing boiler with conventional flue.

Asbestos pipe should not be used for this purpose, due to the fact that certain types can shatter if heated unevenly.

It should be noted that the flue collars are upward, and that the joints are sealed with asbestos rope and fire cement. All types of boiler mentioned in this chapter are available for use with a conventional flue, except some room heaters, which, in any case, are designed for fitting into a fireplace.

Greater flexibility of boiler siting can be achieved by the relatively new development of the balanced flue, and this is shown in Fig. 11.

Potterton Kingfisher gas-fired boiler, with conventional flue.

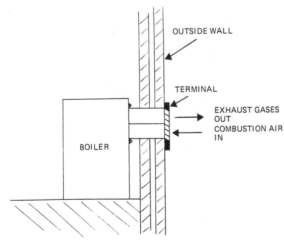

OUTSIDE WALL

TERMINAL

EXHAUST GASES OUT

COMBUSTION AIR IN

BOILER

Fig. 11   Free standing boiler with balanced flue.

33

The boiler is sited against an outside wall, and is connected, via ducting, to a terminal on the outside of the wall. The ducting is in two parts — one to carry the incoming air required for combustion, and the other to expel the exhaust gases. The air movements inside the boiler are therefore entirely separate from those in the room. For this reason, some manufacturers call their products room sealed boilers.

Most balanced flues are designed so that they discharge directly backwards from the boiler, but others are available with the ducts to the left or right. Some models are fitted with fans to assist the air movement.

It is important that the flue terminal is not positioned near to windows or doors, as this could cause the exhaust gases to be admitted to the building.

Balanced flues are available with some oil, and most types of gas fired boilers.

Ideal Concord wall-mounted gas boiler, installed in a kitchen.

Baxi WM wall-mounted gas boiler, installed under a staircase.

FLUE LINERS

The type of conventional flue shown in Fig. 10 would, in fact, be suitable only for solid fuel installations. This is because, with oil and gas boilers, a certain amount of condensation will form inside the brick flue, and this will eventually cause damage.

In existing brick flues, the problem can be solved by fitting a flexible flue liner, as shown in Fig. 12. This is made of thin stainless steel, and a 3ft. length weighs only about one pound. It is sealed to the flue pipe and the terminal so that no exhaust gases can enter the space between the liner and the brick flue.

CONSTRUCTION OF A NEW FLUE

When a new flue is required on an outside wall, the construction shown in Fig. 13 may be the most convenient.

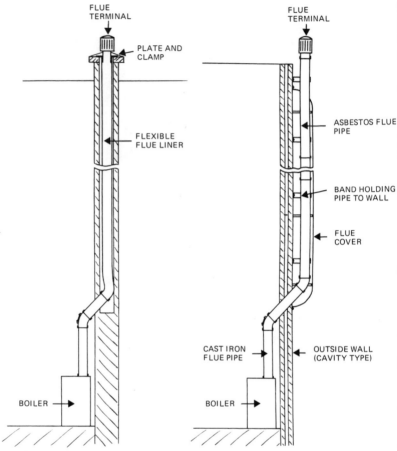

Fig. 12   Conventional flue
with liner.

Fig. 13   Construction of a new
conventional flue on an outside wall.

Here, the flue pipe next to the boiler is made of cast iron,
but asbestos can be used when more than 6ft. from the
boiler. As much as possible of the pipe outside the wall is
covered with an asbestos flue cover. The remaining space
between pipe and cover can be left empty, or filled with
glass fibre insulation. The terminal should be positioned as
high as possible, and away from anything which could cause
a downdraught.

The construction shown can be used for solid fuel or oil
boilers. Because gas boilers produce more flue condensation, it is best to modify the bottom end of the pipe as
shown in Fig. 14.

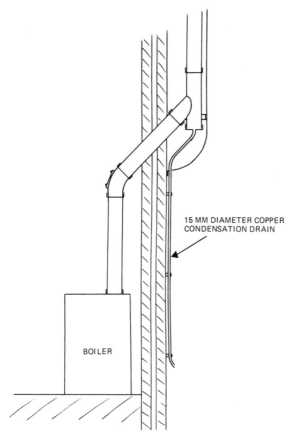

15 MM DIAMETER COPPER
CONDENSATION DRAIN

BOILER

Fig. 14   Flue drain for use with gas boilers.

This allows any excess moisture, which may otherwise
find its way into the boiler, to drain away from the flue pipe.

BOILERS SITED IN GARAGES

It is important to note that, where a boiler is to be
installed in a garage, only a balanced flue type can be used.
This is because:

1. With a conventional flue boiler, petrol fumes could
   be ignited.
2. When a car battery is charged, hydrogen gas is given
   off. This forms an explosive mixture when combined with air. Naked lights, such as from conventional flue boilers (or cigarettes) have been known to
   cause this mixture to explode.

5
DOMESTIC HOT WATER CYLINDERS

The domestic hot water cylinder is a familiar part of any hot water system. It is used as a reservoir in which domestic hot water is stored prior to being delivered to the taps. When running water for a bath, for example, the boiler is not sufficiently powerful to heat the water at that rate. Instead, water that has previously been heated is taken from the cylinder. This is replenished by cold water from the header tank, which results in a drop in temperature of the water in the cylinder. The water in the cylinder is heated up to the original temperature over a period of time following the running of the bath.

There are several distinct types of hot water cylinder.

DIRECT

A typical direct type of hot water cylinder is shown in Fig. 15.

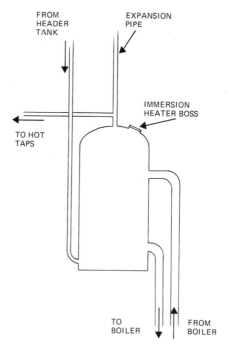

Fig. 15 Domestic hot water cylinder (direct type).

This is as used in any domestic hot water system, but it should not, under any circumstances, be used in a combined hot water and central heating system. This is because:

1. Mains water contains a certain amount of air, and an air/water mixture is all that is required to cause corrosion of metals such as iron and steel. Most boilers contain iron, and steel is used for radiators.

   Fortunately, there is only a certain amount of corrosion which can be caused by a given volume of water. If the water in the boiler and the heating system can be kept separate from the domestic hot water, which is being constantly replenished from the mains, the problem of corrosion will be largely eliminated. The direct type of hot water cylinder has no means of doing this.

2. Mains water also contains a number of impurities which, when the water is heated, cause the formation of scale. If the same water is reheated a number of times, there will eventually be no impurities left to cause further scaling. For this reason, it is desirable to separate the domestic hot water from that used in the heating system.

3. It has been explained that, when a bath is run, the water in the cylinder cools down. If this water is also used in the heating system, the pipework and radiators will cool down at the same time.

INDIRECT

Indirect cylinders are designed to separate the domestic hot water from that circulating through the boiler and the central heating system. Such a cylinder is shown in Fig. 16.

It can be seen that the water circulating through the boiler and heating system is contained inside a tank. This tank is itself surrounded with the water which is contained inside the main cylinder. The heating water (or primary water), and domestic hot water (or secondary water), are thus kept separate.

When the boiler is running, hot water circulates through the inner tank. This, in turn, causes the secondary water to be heated, and after a period of operation, the temperature of the water in both parts will become nearly equal. If a bath is now run, the cooling of the secondary water in the cylinder will cause the temperature of the water returning to the boiler to become somewhat cooler than before. This may cause a slight, but not serious reduction in the water temperature inside the radiators.

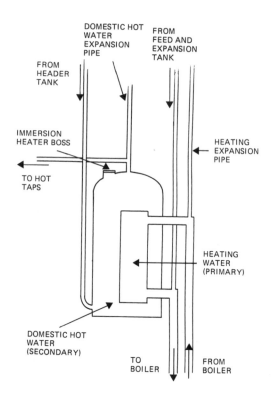

DOMESTIC HOT
WATER
EXPANSION
PIPE

FROM
FEED AND
EXPANSION
TANK

FROM
HEADER
TANK

IMMERSION
HEATER BOSS

HEATING
EXPANSION
PIPE

TO HOT
TAPS

HEATING
WATER
(PRIMARY)

DOMESTIC HOT
WATER
(SECONDARY)

TO
BOILER

FROM
BOILER

Fig. 16   Domestic hot water cylinder (indirect type).

Some indirect cylinders contain an internal coil of pipe, instead of a tank, for the primary water. These operate in exactly the same way, but are preferable in systems where the water flow from the boiler to the cylinder is caused by the action of a pump. This is known as a pumped primary system, and examples are shown in Figs. 3 to 6 (pages 18 to 21).

SELF-PRIMING

These are indirect cylinders, designed for the smaller installation. The primary part of the system is fed and vented automatically, and a feed and expansion tank is no longer required. The pipework arrangement would be as shown in Fig. 15.

These cylinders offer a useful alternative to a sealed system for use in flats and smaller properties. However, they cannot be used in pumped primary systems, and are confined to gravity primary systems similar to that shown in Fig. 43 (page 84).

The main disadvantage of these cylinders is that if the water boils, the primary and secondary waters will mix. Installation into systems fired by solid fuel boilers cannot be recommended for this reason.

CONVERSION UNITS

For microbore, and pumped primary small bore systems, it is possible to change an existing direct hot water cylinder into an indirect one. This requires the use of a conversion unit, which fits into the immersion heater boss, as shown in Fig. 17.

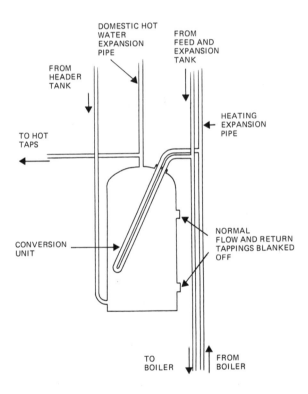

Fig. 17 Hot water cylinder conversion unit, with small bore pipe feed.

HOT WATER TEMPERATURE CONTROLS

Earlier in this chapter, it was shown that, after a period of operation, the domestic hot water reaches nearly the same temperature as the primary water. The primary water temperature, in turn, is controlled by the boiler thermostat.

It must be remembered that water at a temperature of 140°F can scald, but the boiler thermostat will need to be set greatly in excess of this figure if the heating system is to attain the required room temperatures. Some method of controlling the temperature of the domestic hot water at some level below that set on the boiler thermostat is highly desirable, if not essential. It is important to note, however, that systems fired by solid fuel boilers cannot be fitted with such controls. This is because they require a route by which any excess heat can be easily dispersed.

Temperature controls can be of either electrical or mechanical type. Electrical methods are more complicated, but have a number of additional advantages. They are described in Chapter 13.

Mechanical controls are self-contained, and are simply fitted into the pipework between the boiler and the hot water cylinder. They operate by sensing the temperature of the water in the pipe, and the temperature at which they are set is adjustable on a dial.

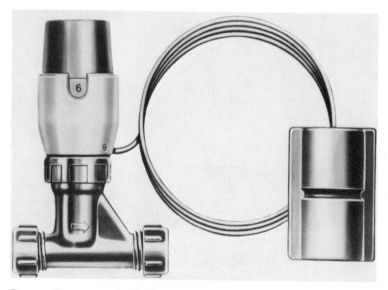

Drayton Tapstat mechanical controller for domestic hot water, for use in pumped primary systems.

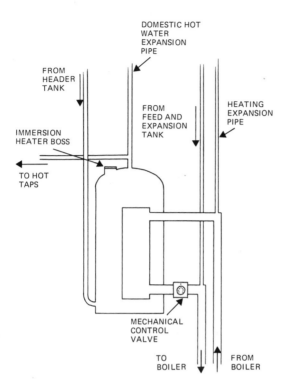

DOMESTIC HOT
WATER
EXPANSION
PIPE

FROM
HEADER
TANK

FROM
FEED AND
EXPANSION
TANK

HEATING
EXPANSION
PIPE

IMMERSION
HEATER BOSS

TO HOT
TAPS

MECHANICAL
CONTROL
VALVE

TO
BOILER

FROM
BOILER

Fig. 18   Siting of mechanical hot water temperature control valve.

The valve shown in Fig. 18 is positioned in the return
pipe, as near to the cylinder as possible. As the secondary
water is warmed up, the temperature of the water passing
through the valve increases until the level set on the dial is
reached. At this point, the valve closes, thus stopping the
flow.

As the pipework cools, a point will be reached where the
valve opens again. Flow is resumed, and the secondary
water will receive heat. The secondary water is thus controlled at some temperature below that of the primary water.

6
RADIATORS

The modern radiator, made from pressed steel, is well known. Unlike the older, cast iron variety, it is both reasonable in appearance and easy to paint. On the other hand, the relative thinness of the steel and the quality of welding sometimes cause minor leaks to develop. Most merchants can supply radiators which are curved or angled for fitting into bay windows. These should be treated with caution, as the bending process can cause additional stresses leading to leakage.

EMISSION AND SIZING

In the past, the heat output, or emission, from a radiator was calculated in accordance with its surface area. Today, manufacturers state an emission figure for each radiator in their range, and it is safer to use this. By reference to any such list, it will be seen that a double panel radiator does not emit exactly twice the amount of heat of a single panel type of the same height and width.

The emission depends on the temperature of the water inside the radiator. This is usually based on a difference of 100 °F between the water and the air in the room. In a living room at 70°F, the average water temperature should therefore be 170°F. It is usual, also, to allow the water to cool by 20°F as it passes through the radiator. This means that the boiler thermostat should be set at 180°F.

Under these conditions, the emission figures stated by a radiator manufacturer can be used for any room which is required to be heated to 70°F. However, for a bedroom at 60°F, there will be an 110°F average temperature difference between the water and the air in the room. This results in the emission figure being raised, and the radiator size being reduced. The factors are:

For a room temperature of 60°F, multiply emission by 1·13, or divide heat loss by 1·13.

For a room temperature of 65°F, multiply emission by 1·07, or divide heat loss by 1·07.

These are used as follows. Suppose that calculations of the type shown in Chapter 2 have been carried out, and a bedroom is known to have a heat loss of 4,402 B.Th.Us. per hour. This is to be heated to a temperature of 60°F by one radiator, 24in. high. How wide must the radiator be?

Heat loss is 4,402 B.Th.Us. per hour.
Corrected heat loss (for radiator sizing) is
$$4,402 \div 1\cdot13$$
$$= 3,896 \text{ B.Th.Us. per hour.}$$
From one manufacturer's tables, a single panel radiator, 24in. high and 59in. wide gives an emission of 4,050 B.Th.Us. per hour.

Therefore the radiator, if produced by this manufacturer, needs to be 59in. wide (single panel).

If the calculated width of 59in. is too great, a double panel radiator must be used.

Although radiators of up to about 12,000 B.Th.Us. per hour emission are available, it is usual to use two radiators for rooms with a heat loss greater than about 9,000 B.Th.Us. per hour. The shape of rooms must also be considered. The lounge of the house shown in Fig. 2 (page 12) will need a radiator near to each end.

BOILER EMISSION

Any boiler will emit a certain amount of heat into the surrounding space. If the boiler is sited in a kitchen, this can be taken into account in order to reduce the size of the kitchen radiator. The amount of emission varies, and the specification of the boiler to be used should be consulted.

For the kitchen of the house in Chapter 2, the radiator would be sized as follows, assuming that the boiler to be used emits 2·5% of its rated output.

Kitchen heat loss is 4,314 B.Th.Us. per hour.
Output of boiler is 53,500 B.Th.Us. per hour.
Therefore emission from the boiler is
$$2\cdot5\% \text{ of } 53,500$$
$$= (2\cdot5 \div 100) \times 53,500$$
$$= 1,338 \text{ B.Th.Us. per hour}$$
Therefore the heat loss to be made good by the radiator is
$$4,314 - 1,338$$
$$= 2,976 \text{ B.Th.Us. per hour.}$$
But designed kitchen temperature is 65°F.
So corrected heat loss (for radiator sizing) is
$$2,976 \div 1\cdot07$$
$$= 2,781 \text{ B.Th.Us. per hour}$$
A single panel radiator of about 30in. height and 33in. width would be sufficient for this.

It is important to note that the corrected heat losses above must be used only for radiator sizing. The room heat losses are still as calculated in Chapter 2.

Hot water cylinders should be heavily lagged to prevent

heat loss. Because of this, it is not usual to reduce the radiator size in the room in which the cylinder is sited.

RADIATOR TAPPINGS AND VALVES

Single panel radiators are equipped with either three or four female threads at the corners. These are known as tappings, and are used for connecting the radiator to the system. A typical arrangement is shown in Fig. 19, and the use of each tapping is as follows:

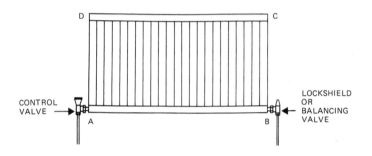

Fig. 19   Position of tappings in a single panel radiator.

Tapping A   is used for the radiator control valve. This is the valve by which the radiator is turned on or off, or regulated to some intermediate setting.

Tapping B   is used for the balancing, or lockshield, valve. This is adjusted when the system is running to give the correct water flow through the radiator. It is then either locked, or fitted with a plastic cover to avoid accidental readjustment.

The use of tappings A and B can be reversed if required. It should be noted that the flow and return pipes are both connected to tappings at the bottom of the radiator. This is adequate for any heating system through which the water is moved by a pump. In any case, few modern radiators have tappings at C or D which are large enough to accept the threads of control or lockshield valves.

Most control and lockshield valves are arranged to be easily disconnected from the radiator. If both valves are first closed, and then disconnected, the radiator may be easily removed when decorating. Only the water inside the radiator itself needs to be drained off.

Tapping C is used for the radiator bleed valve. Any air in the system will eventually find its way to the highest points, and this is often the top of each radiator. The bleed valve, which is used to remove this trapped air, is operated by a key.

Tapping D is not required, and must be fitted with a blanking plug.

Again, the use of tappings C and D can be reversed. Some radiators are fitted with one upper tapping only, the opposite end being blanked off. In this case, the bleed valve must be fitted into the only upper tapping available.

Double panel radiators are slightly different, as shown in Fig. 20.

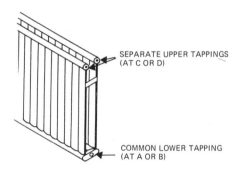

Fig. 20   Double panel radiator tappings.

Myson radiator with integral towel rail. The control valve (right) and lockshield valve (left) can be clearly seen.

Honeywell Y508A thermostatic radiator valve. Self-contained and remote temperature sensors are available.

Myson thermostatic radiator valve.

Damixa thermostatic radiator valve. Note the arrow showing the direction of water flow.

Drayton TRV2 thermostatic radiator valve with self-contained temperature sensor. Types with remote sensor are available.

Most have single lower tappings in positions A and B, and double upper tappings in positions C and D. Two bleed valves will be required for this type, and possibly two blanking plugs.

A hexagonal wrench (allen key) is required to fit most control and lockshield valves into radiators.

COMBINED VALVES FOR MICROBORE SYSTEMS

Radiators on microbore systems may be installed basically as above, except that the control and lockshield valves need to be fitted with reducing unions to accept the smaller flow and return pipes. This is probably the best method.

However, combined, or bi-action valves as they are sometimes called, are available. An example is shown in Fig. 21.

A nylon pipe is inserted into the bottom of the radiator which delivers the incoming water to the far end. This should be arranged to give a gap of about 3in. as shown. After passing through the radiator, the water flows out via

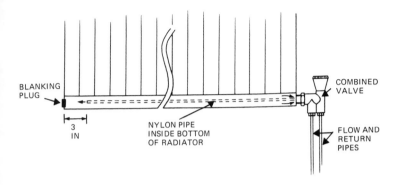

Fig. 21   Combined radiator valve for microbore systems.

the space between the nylon pipe and the valve body, and into the return pipe.

It is important to note the length of the nylon pipe. If this is too long, the flow of water from it may be impeded. Too short a length can result in the radiator only reaching the correct surface temperature at the end nearest to the valve.

The fitting of combined valves into double panel radiators can sometimes cause a problem, due to the nylon pipe. Fig. 22 shows the bottom of a double panel radiator looking from above.

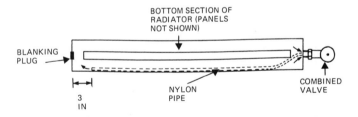

Fig. 22   Combined valve, fitted to double panel radiator (view from above).

It will be seen that two sharp bends are required in the nylon pipe, near to the combined valve. These bends may have to be so sharp that the pipe collapses, thus stopping the water flow.

TEMPERATURE CONTROLS

Earlier in this chapter, it was explained that the boiler thermostat controls the water temperature in the radiators.

The occupants of a room are interested not in radiator temperature, but in the air temperature in the room. Ideally, room temperature controls should thus be designed to monitor the air temperature.

Such controls may be of either electrical or mechanical type. Electrical methods are more complicated, but have a number of additional advantages. They are described in Chapter 13.

Mechanical controls are confined to thermostatic radiator valves, which take the place of the usual control valve. They are often self-contained, but some models are available with remote temperature sensors. As the temperature of the radiator itself may influence the operation of the self-contained types, those with remote sensors are preferable.

SITING OF RADIATORS

There are many arguments centered around the siting of radiators, and these mainly boil down to whether or not they should be positioned below windows. Either way, there are a certain number of disadvantages, and it is really a matter of personal preference.

Disadvantages of siting below windows are:
1. By reference to the U-values in Chapter 1, page 8, it can be seen that even double glazed windows will allow the loss of more heat than any type of wall. A greater amount of heat emitted by the radiator will thus be lost through the glass.
2. A certain amount of emitted heat will be lost through the wall to the outside. This is not the case with a radiator on an internal wall, as the heat lost through the wall will be gained by the adjoining room.
3. Flow and return pipes may need to be long.
4. Curtains may be difficult to hang.

Disadvantages of siting on internal walls are:
5. Draughts passing through window frames may be troublesome. When a radiator is sited below a window, draughts are warmed and become less noticeable.
6. Furniture should not be placed in front of radiators, and rearrangement may be necessary.
7. If a shelf is not fitted above the radiator, the wall above may become dirty.

Any radiator sited on an outside wall, but not below a window, can suffer from 2, 3, 5, 6 and 7 above.

7
SKIRTING HEATERS AND FAN-CONVECTORS

As explained in Chapter 2, panel radiators cannot be used with sealed systems which are designed to run at high temperatures. This is because they are heated to such a high temperature that anyone touching them would be burned.

Skirting heaters and fan-convectors, however, are ideal for use in high temperature systems. This is because their hot parts are protected by a decorative casing. Exposed flow and return pipes should still be covered in some way.

Systems operating at normal temperatures may also use skirting heaters and fan-convectors. Either could be used where wall area required by radiators is limited. Skirting heaters, due to their low height, may be the only type of heating unit which can be installed below a large window.

Skirting heater casings are available with both internal and external corners, thus enabling any required length to follow around the walls.

HEAT EXCHANGERS

Skirting heaters and fan-convectors both contain a device known as a heat exchanger. This is a general name which is given to any unit which is designed to exchange heat from one thing to another. The domestic radiator can be regarded as a type of heat exchanger, because it is designed to exchange heat from the hot water which it contains, to the surrounding air.

The type of heat exchanger fitted into skirting heaters and fan-convectors is fairly small, and the construction can be seen in Fig. 23.

A series of thin metal fins are either held mechanically, or brazed on to a pipe. The pipe forms part of the heating system, and hot water is passed through it. After a period of operation, the pipe and fins reach almost the same temperature as the water. Any air passing between the fins will be warmed, resulting in a decrease in the temperature of the assembly. Heat is thus lost from the water, and gained by the air.

The amount of heat exchanged depends, among other things, on the surface area of the fins. For any overall fin size, there are two methods by which a manufacturer can increase the effective surface area, and they are:

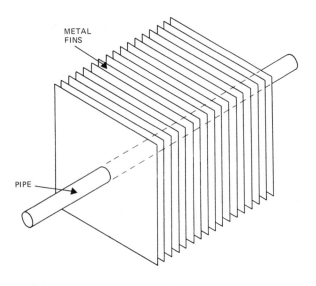

Fig. 23   Construction of a heat exchanger.

    1. Increase the number of fins. That is, space them closer together.
    2. Fit fins which are not flat, but corrugated.

Heat exchangers fitted into skirting heaters are usually referred to as elements.

SKIRTING HEATERS

The cross-section of a typical skirting heater is shown in fig. 24.

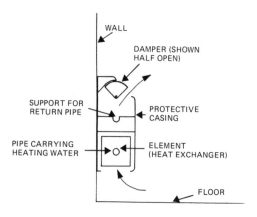

Fig. 24   Cross section of a typical skirting heater.

Myson Wallstrip 'S' skirting heater, installed into a corner. Note the low level of the window sill.

When the heating system is in operation, air passes through the element by the natural process of convection. This airflow can be reduced if required by partially closing the damper, which results in a reduction of heat emission. Skirting heaters are, of course, completely silent in operation.

The pipe passing through the element is usually of 15mm. or 22mm. diameter. When the return pipe needs to run back along the length of the heater, it should be positioned in the supports provided. Built-in protection against burning is thus obtained.

Where skirting heaters are piped individually, control valves and lockshield valves are required for each. If a loop type circulation is used, as shown in Fig. 49 (page 89), such valves cannot be fitted as the water flow through the whole loop would be affected.

SKIRTING HEATER EMISSION

Each skirting heater manufacturer states the emission of his product in B.Th.Us. per hour per foot. Unlike radiators, tables are usually given which show the emission obtained for various water and room temperatures, and so correction is not necessary. For a heating system using both radiators and skirting heaters, it is reasonable to use an average water temperature of 170°F. Figures given are usually based on the skirting heater damper being fully open, and an assumed water flow rate through the element is also sometimes given. Water flow rate is dealt with in Chapter 8.

The emission figures are used as follows. Suppose that calculations of the type shown in Chapter 2 have been carried out, and a bedroom is known to have a heat loss of 4,402 B.Th.Us. per hour. This is to be heated to a temperature of 60°F by a skirting heater. How long must the heater be?

Heat loss is 4,402 B.Th. Us. per hour.

Emission of a skirting heater with an average water temperature of 170°F, and a room temperature of 60°F is 450 B.Th.Us. per hour per foot. (manufacturer's figure).

Therefore the length of heater is 4,402 ÷ 450
= 9·78 feet.

Therefore a length of 10ft. will be adequate.

It should be noted that skirting heaters are available in two parts — element only and casing only. The element can thus be shorter than the casing to allow for pipe bends, connections or valves. The calculated figure of 9·78ft. above applies to the length of the element, and not the length of the casing. As with radiators, more than one length of heater can be used in any room.

FAN-CONVECTORS

The heat exchanger fitted to most fan-convectors is similar to that shown in Fig. 23. In order to use larger fins and give better exchange of heat, several pipes are used. Each is bent, and made to pass through the fins more than once.

This is shown in Figs. 25 and 26.

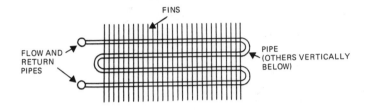

Fig. 25   Heat exchanger, as fitted to a fan convector (view from above).

Fig. 26 shows the main parts of a fan-convector. Here, the air is blown through the heat exchanger by the fan. Even when the fan is not running, a reduced amount of heat is emitted by natural convection. Depending on the speed of the fan, the unit makes a noise similar to that from an electric fan heater.

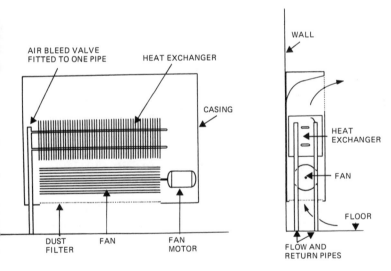

Fig. 26   A typical fan convector.

It is usual for the manufacturer to fit a number of controls, and they are:

    1. Fan speed control. This controls the speed at which the fan rotates, and an off position is also provided.

Myson Minivector horizontal fan-convector.

2. An adjustable room air temperature thermostat, which causes the fan to be switched on or off as required. Provision is also usually made for a remote thermostat, if preferred, and this should give even better control of the room air temperature.

3. A winter/summer switch. In the winter position, an internal thermostat is used to sense the water temperature. If the flow becomes cool for any reason, the fan is switched off to prevent unheated air being blown around the room. The summer position bypasses this thermostat and allows the fan to be used to circulate unheated air.

Due to the design and operation of fan-convectors, the heating system to which they are connected must satisfy several requirements. They are:

1. An internal room air temperature thermostat is provided, or a remote one may be connected. Either way, the fan-convector will control its own heat emission. Room thermostats controlling the remainder of the system should not be sited in any room containing fan-convectors.

2. A constant supply of hot water is required during heating periods, otherwise the water temperature thermostat will stop the fan. The boiler will switch on and off due to its own thermostat, but it cannot be switched off externally until the end of the heating period, for example, at bedtime. Similarly, the

method of temperature control by switching the pump on or off cannot be used. A rather more complicated control circuit is required, and this is described in Chapter 13 (page 100).

It is usual, when installing a fan-convector, to fit a valve in both the flow and return pipes. These are not intended to be control valves, but may be used for balancing when more than one fan-convector is installed. Special valves for this purpose are available from fan-convector manufacturers.

Fig. 26 shows a unit installed just above floor level. Models are available for mounting at high level.

FAN-CONVECTOR EMISSION

Emission is again quoted by the individual manufacturer, and is dependent on the size of the unit, fan speed, water temperature and water flow rate.

It is advisable to select a fan-convector which is capable of making good the heat loss from a room when the fan speed is low. This will enable a rapid warm-up of a cold room to be achieved by setting the fan to a high speed.

Myson vertical fan-convector, which is especially useful where space available for heating units is limited.

8
PIPES

For some years, the plumbing in new buildings has been carried out using copper pipe. This material has certain advantages, in that it is reasonably easy to cut, solder and bend. In recent years, however, copper has become very expensive, and has occasionally been in short supply. Because of this, some stainless steel pipe is now being used for domestic plumbing. Cutting, soldering and bending are still possible, but these operations tend to be more difficult than with copper.

PIPE SIZES

Copper and stainless steel pipes are now sold in metric sizes, and these replace the old imperial sizes. Pipe diameters normally used in domestic installations are:

35mm. — replaces 1¼ inch ⎫
28mm. — replaces 1 inch ⎪
22mm. — replaces ¾ inch ⎬ small bore.
15mm. — replaces ½ inch ⎭

10mm. — replaces ⅜ inch ⎫
8mm. ⎬ microbore — copper
6mm. — replaces ¼ inch ⎭ only

It is usual for the small bore pipes above to be supplied in straight lengths, and the microbore pipes in coils.

SMALL BORE PIPES

For any given water speed, it is obvious that a large pipe will carry more water than a smaller one. In heating applications, the water speed needs to be limited, otherwise noise and vibration will be set up. The generally accepted figures for water carrying capacity are as follows:

28mm. will carry up to 340 gallons per hour.
22mm. will carry up to 190 gallons per hour.
15mm. will carry up to 75 gallons per hour.

Using this information, it is possible to calculate the heat carrying capacity of any pipe. For the 22mm. diameter shown above:

One gallon of water weighs ten pounds.
The pipe will carry 190 gallons per hour.
Therefore the weight of water carried in 10 × 190
= 1,900 pounds per hour.

If water cools by 20°F as it passes through the system,

amount of heat released is 1,900 × 20
$$= 38,000 \text{ B.Th.Us. per hour.}$$
By carrying out similar calculations, the heat carrying capacity of the 28mm. and 15mm. sizes can be found. These are stated below.

When water is passed through any pipe, a certain amount of resistance to the flow is set up. This is known as friction, and the effect changes as follows:

1. As pipe diameter increases, friction decreases.
2. As pipe length increases, friction increases.
3. Straight pipe is best, bends increase friction.
4. Sharp bends and elbows cause more friction to be set up than sweep bends.

The total friction set up in the pipework must be overcome by the pump. This does not normally cause any problem in small bore systems if the maximum pipe lengths stated below are observed.

Summarising, the following heat carrying capacities and pipe lengths should be observed:

28mm. up to 68,000 B.Th.Us. per hour and 140ft. long.
22mm. up to 38,000 B.Th.Us. per hour and 100ft. long.
15mm. up to 15,000 B.Th.Us. per hour and 80ft. long.

These figures are used as follows. Three radiators, each emitting 6,000 B.Th.Us. per hour, are to be connected using a pair of pipes. What diameter do the pipes need to be?

A diagram will be found helpful, and this is shown in Fig. 27(a).

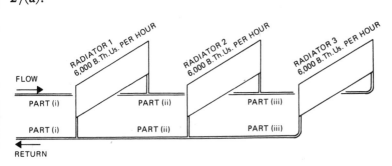

Fig. 27 (a)   Diagram for pipe sizing calculation.

The problem must be solved in three parts:
(i) Pipes to and from the boiler.
Heating load is 6,000 + 6,000 + 6,000
$$= 18,000 \text{ B.Th.Us. per hour.}$$
This is too great a load for 15mm. diameter pipes, so 22mm. diameter will be required for this part.

(ii) Pipes from radiator 1 to radiator 2.
Heating load is 6,000+6,000
= 12,000 B.Th.Us. per hour.
15mm. diameter pipes will be adequate here.
(iii) Pipes from radiator 2 to radiator 3.
Heating load is 6,000 B.Th.Us. per hour.
15mm. diameter pipes will be adequate here.

If the total pipe length, that is, the length of both pipes added together, from the boiler to radiator 1 does not exceed 100ft., 22mm. diameter pipes can be used for part (i). Similarly, if the total pipe length from radiator 1 to radiator 3 does not exceed 80ft., 15mm. diameter pipes can be used for parts (ii) and (iii). In the unlikely event of either length being exceeded, the next larger pipe diameter must be used.

The diagram can now be altered to show the pipe sizes, as in Fig. 27(b).

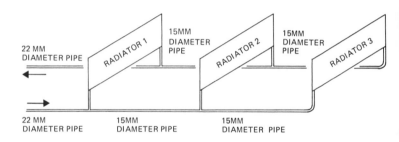

Fig. 27 (b)   Solution to pipe sizing calculation.

MICROBORE PIPES

Because of their smaller diameter, microbore pipes cannot carry as much water as small bore ones. This is partly offset by the fact that special pumps are now available for use with mircobore systems.

The smaller diameters also lead to increased friction, and pipe lengths become more critical. For a pipe length of 50ft., the accepted figures for water carrying capacity are:

10mm. will carry up to 35 gallons per hour.
8mm. will carry up to 20 gallons per hour.
6mm. will carry up to 9 gallons per hour.

The resulting heat carrying capacities can now be calculated exactly as for small bore pipes. However, it is possible to obtain higher figures if the pipe lengths can be kept shorter than 50ft. This is because the resulting lower friction values will allow a greater volume of water to be passed along the pipe. The resulting capacities can be found from the graph in Fig. 28.

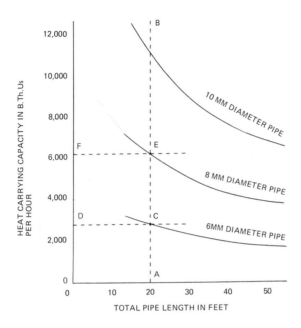

Fig. 28   Sizing graph for microbore pipes.

The graph is used as follows. Suppose that, in a micro-bore system, the total pipe length from a manifold to a radiator, and back again, is 20ft. The radiator is designed to emit 5,000 B.Th.Us. per hour. What diameter of microbore pipe will be required?

The vertical line AB is drawn on the graph through the 20ft. mark.

C is the point where AB crosses the 6mm. pipe line.

The horizontal line DC is drawn.

D indicates the capacity of the pipe, which is 2,900 B.Th.Us. per hour.

This is less than the designed emission of the radiator, so this pipe is not large enough.

Similarly, FE is drawn.

F indicates the capacity of the pipe, which is 6,400 B.Th.Us. per hour.

This is greater than the designed emission of the radiator, so 8mm. diameter pipe is adequate.

If necessary, the 10mm. diameter pipe would be treated in exactly the same way.

These figures, which assume a 20°F temperature drop of the water in each radiator, result in the smaller diameter pipes becoming almost useless. For this reason, some microbore systems are designed with a 30°F, or even 40°F temperature drop. This results in the boiler thermostat needing to be set at 185°F (30°F drop), or 190°F (40°F drop), and such temperatures are only really safe in a sealed, pressurized system.

PIPES FEEDING DOMESTIC HOT WATER CYLINDERS

In Chapter 2, the amount of heat required for the domestic hot water was calculated. depending on the reheat period and cylinder capacity, this will usually amount to about 10,000 B.Th.Us. per hour. The pipework connecting the cylinder to the boiler must be capable of carrying this heat load.

In pumped primary systems, the pump is used to draw water through the heating coil in the hot water cylinder. Here, the cylinder may be regarded simply as a radiator of about 10,000 B.Th.Us. per hour emission. The flow and return pipes can thus be sized exactly as shown earlier in this chapter.

Where a pump is not used, the circulation of water from the boiler through the hot water cylinder takes place by gravity. This is known as a gravity primary system. In order to cause less friction against this gravity flow, pipes of larger diameter are used. The actual diameter depends on the horizontal and vertical distances from the cylinder to the boiler. The domestic hot water capacity of the cylinder also has an effect, and the graph shown in Fig. 29 is for a cylinder holding 30 gallons.

The graph is used as follows. Suppose that a 30 gallon hot water cylinder is positioned 8ft. above, and 5ft. sideways from the boiler. The system is of the gravity primary type. What diameter must the flow and return pipes be?

The vertical height from the boiler to the cylinder is 8ft. This is drawn on the graph, and is shown by the line AB.

The horizontal distance from the boiler to the cylinder is 5ft. This is drawn on the graph, and is shown by the line CD.

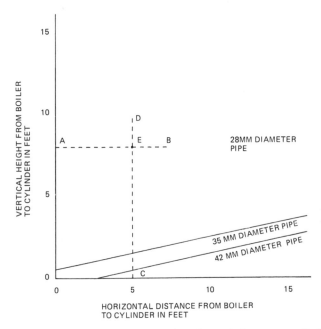

Fig. 29   Pipe sizing graph, for 30 gallon domestic hot water cylinders used in gravity primary systems.

The two lines cross at E, and this lies in the area marked — 28mm. diameter pipe.

So the required pipe size for this installation is 28mm. diameter.

HEAT EMISSION FROM PIPES

Like radiators, pipes emit a certain amount of heat. Where this occurs in a room, for example, the emission is not important, as it contributes to the heating of the room. In practice, a slight heat loss from the circulating water will take place, but this has been allowed for in the heat capacities stated previously for pipes, in this chapter.

On the other hand, a substantial amount of heat can be lost where pipes run through an unheated space such as a loft. With an outside temperature of 30°F, and average water temperature of 170°F, the loss for unlagged pipes is about:

28mm. — 74 B.Th.Us. per hour per foot.
22mm. — 58 B.Th.Us. per hour per foot.
15mm. — 38 B.Th.Us. per hour per foot.
10mm. — 26 B.Th.Us. per hour per foot.
8mm. — 20 B.Th.Us. per hour per foot.
6mm. — 16 B.Th.Us. per hour per foot.

When the resulting heat loss is large, it should be compensated for in the pipe and boiler sizing calculations.

9
CIRCULATION PUMPS

Circulation pumps, or circulators as they are sometimes called, are used in modern central heating systems to propel the water through the pipework and heating units. In some systems, the pump is also used to move water through the heating coil in the domestic hot water cylinder. The systems shown in Chapter 3 are all examples of this.

The pump itself consists mainly of an electric motor. this drives an impellor, which is similar to that fitted inside the water pump of a motor car. Attention is not normally required in service, but several points should be observed if best life and performance are to be achieved:

1. A certain amount of sediment is present in all heating systems, which eventually finds its way to the lowest point. In order to keep the pump as free from obstruction as possible, it should be positioned at some higher level.
2. A valve should be fitted into the pipework on each side of the pump. This enables the unit to be removed without draining the water from the whole of the system.
3. The pump should be positioned so that the air bleed screw is at the highest point on the unit.

STATIC HEAD

It is important to note that static head has nothing whatever to do with the performance of the circulation pump. However, it is often confused with dynamic head, which follows.

Fig. 30 shows a header tank connected to a section of pipework. If a hole is punched in the pipe at A, water will spurt out under pressure. This pressure is produced by the height of the water above A, and it should be noted that neither the pipe diameter nor the size of the header tank will have any effect.

In the case shown, the pressure at A will be 24ft. water gauge (w.g.). This means that the pressure exerted at A is capable of supporting a column of water 24ft. high.

If A is, in fact, at the lowest point on the system, the system is said to be subject to a static head of 24ft. water gauge. As long as the header tank is filled to the normal water level, this static head is exerted in all directions, and at all times.

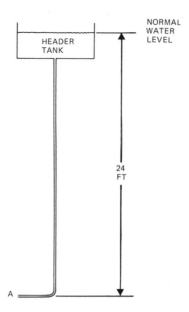

Fig. 30   Static head of a water system.

In a sealed system, it is static head which is produced by the action of the pressure vessel. See Chapter 10 (page 76).

DYNAMIC HEAD

Dynamic head is the pressure set up in a water system by the action of a pump. This is again measured in water gauge. If a pump is capable of supporting a column of water 5ft. high, it is said to exert a dynamic head of 5ft. water gauge.

In a heating system, the pump is not required to support a column of water. The whole of the dynamic head which is exerted can be used to overcome the resistance set up against the water flow as it passes through the system. This resistance is mainly caused by friction inside the pipes. Friction in water pipes is also measured in feet water gauge. For the water to move along the pipe, the dynamic head produced by the pump must be greater than the friction set up in the pipe.

FRICTION IN PIPES

In a straight pipe, the amount of friction set up depends on the flow rate of the water, and the length of the pipe. The flow rate can be associated with the amount of heat being carried by the pipe. See Chapter 8 (page 60).

Bends and fittings in the pipe have the effect of increasing the amount of friction set up. It would be possible to find the amount set up by each bend and fitting, and add them together. In practice, the total friction set up in straight pipes is increased by one-third to allow for these.

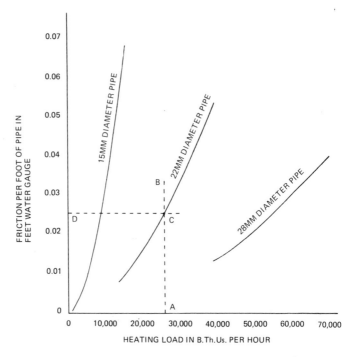

Fig. 31   Pipe friction graph, for systems with 20°F temperature drop

The graph shown in Fig. 31 may be used for a heating system with a water temperature drop of 20°F through each heating unit. The one-third allowance for bends and fittings has been included.

The graph is used as follows. Suppose that a 10ft. length of 22mm. diameter pipe is carrying 25,000 B.Th.Us. of heat per hour. How much friction is set up in the pipe?

The vertical line AB is drawn on the graph through the 25,000 B.Th.Us. per hour mark.

C is the point where AB crosses the 22mm. diameter pipe line.

The horizontal line DC is drawn.

D indicates the amount of friction set up in the pipe, which is 0·025ft. water gauge per foot.

68

But the pipe is 10ft. long.
So the total friction is 0·025 × 10
$$= 0·25ft. \text{ water gauge.}$$

THE INDEX CIRCUIT

Suppose that for a heating installation, the heat losses from the rooms have been calculated as shown in Chapter 2. The heating units have been sized, and the pipe runs planned. The pipe lengths and diameters are thus known. A simplified system is shown in Fig. 32.

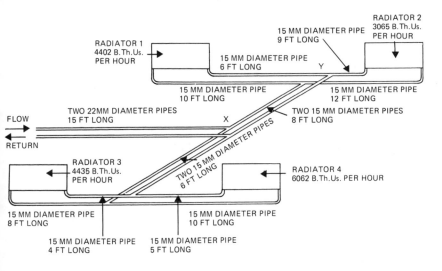

Fig. 32 Simplified pipe and radiator layout for a heating system (twin pipe circulation).

For the moment, ignore radiators 2, 3 and 4. For radiator 1, water leaving the boiler must pass through 30ft. of 22mm. diameter pipe, and 32ft. of 15mm. diameter pipe before it arrives back at the boiler again. Using the graph in Fig. 31, the total friction set up in this circuit is calculated as follows:

The two 22mm. diameter pipes carry 17,964 B.Th.Us. per hour over 15ft.

Friction set up is 0·014ft. water gauge per foot (from graph).

So the friction set up in the 22mm. diameter pipes is
$$0·014 × 2 × 15$$
$$= 0·42ft. \text{ water gauge.}$$

The two 15mm. diameter pipes from X to Y carry 7,467 B.Th.Us. per hour over 8ft.

Friction set up is 0·02ft. water gauge per foot (from graph).

So the total friction set up in section XY is 0·02 × 2 × 8
$$= 0·32\text{ft. water gauge.}$$

The 15mm. diameter pipe from Y, through radiator 1, and back to Y carries 4,402 B.Th.Us. per hour over 16ft.

Friction set up is 0·008ft. water gauge per foot (from graph).

So the friction set up in the section from Y to radiator 1 is
$$0·008 × 16$$
$$= 0·128\text{ft. water gauge.}$$

Therefore the total friction set up in the circuit through radiator 1 is
$$0·42 + 0·32 + 0·128$$
$$= 0·868\text{ft. water gauge.}$$

The total friction set up in the circuits through radiators 2, 3 and 4 is found in exactly the same way. In this example, they are:

Radiator 2 is 0·835ft. water gauge.

Radiator 3 is 0·948ft. water gauge.

Radiator 4 is 1·062ft. water gauge.

By comparing the above figures, it can be seen that the greatest friction is set up in the circuit through radiator 4. This circuit of greatest friction is known as the index circuit.

If the system in Fig. 32 were operating, most of the hot water from the boiler would pass through the circuit in which the least friction was set up. Thus, radiator 2 would attain the highest temperature, and radiator 4, the lowest. This problem is corrected by opening the lockshield valve fully on radiator 4, and partially closing them on radiators 1, 2 and 3. This causes the friction set up in each circuit to become equal to that in the index circuit.

It is sometimes possible to decide which the index circuit will be, without carrying out a long series of calculations. If in doubt, the friction set up in each should be found, and the totals compared as above.

PUMP SELECTION AND SETTING

Some years ago, circulation pumps were made to give a fixed dynamic head. Careful calculation of the friction set up in the pipework was necessary in order that the correct pump could be selected.

Myson Unit Two central heating pump.

Today, pumps are made to give a variable dynamic head, and adjustment is easy. Most models will be adequate for any domestic heating installation. In some cases, boilers are sold complete with pumps, and no different choice is possible. Because of this, it is now not so necessary to carry out calculations for the selection of the pump.

For those who wish to carry out the calculations, the method is shown in this section. This is for a typical small bore installation. Consider the total heating load of a building, as calculated in Chapter 2. The figures were:

Lounge	11,844
Kitchen	4,314
Hall, landing and stairs	6,381
Bedroom 1	4,402
Bedroom 2	3,065
Bedroom 3	2,435
Bathroom	4,062
Hot water (30 gallons, 3 hour reheat)	10,000
Therefore the total heating load is	46,503
15% allowance (gas boiler, intermittent)	6,975
	53,478 B.Th.Us. per hr.

If the circulation of water through the heating coil in the hot water cylinder is pumped, the pump must be capable of delivering 53,478 B.Th.Us. per hour of heat into the system. This can be reduced to 43,478 B.Th.Us. per hour in gravity primary systems. It should be noted that the boiler allowance of 6,975 B.Th.Us. per hour remains in either case. This is an allowance to cope with very low outside temperatures, and the pump may be required to deliver it.

In a system where the water temperature drop through the heating units is 20°F, it has been shown that each gallon of water gives out 200 B.Th.Us. If, as in the above example, the total pump load is 43,478 B.Th.Us. per hour, the pump must deliver: 43,478 ÷ 200

$$= 217 \cdot 39 \text{ gallons per hour.}$$
$$= 3 \cdot 62 \text{ gallons per minute.}$$

A performance graph for the proposed pump, of the type shown in Fig. 33 is now required.

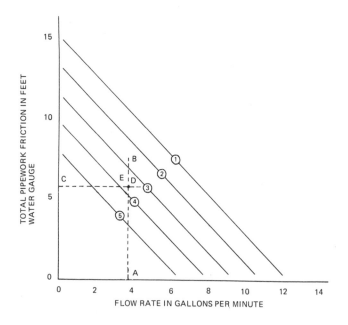

Fig. 33   A typical pump performance graph.

This gives various items of information, and is used as follows. Suppose that the above heating system has an index circuit friction of 5ft. water gauge. The pump must deliver 3·62 gallons per minute.

The friction value, if calculated as previously shown in this chapter, was for an outside temperature of 30°F. A 15% boiler allowance was added to cope with lower temperatures, and the index circuit friction must also be increased by this amount.

Index circuit friction is . . . . .   5·0

15% allowance . . . .   0·75

———

5·75ft. water gauge.

Then, the vertical line AB is drawn on the graph, through the 3·62 gallons per hour mark.

The horizontal line CD is drawn through the 5·75ft. water gauge mark.

The two lines cross at E.

Because E lies between the diagonal lines 1 and 5 on the graph, the proposed pump is suitable for the installation. If E lay above the diagonal line 1, or below the diagonal line 5, the pump would not be suitable.

The diagonal lines represent the pump settings. The pump should be set to just below number 4.

POSITIONING THE PUMP IN THE PIPEWORK

When a pump is running, two effects are produced in the pipework. For every gallon of water which the pump propels in one direction, it draws one gallon from the opposite direction. A positive dynamic head is thus produced on the pressure side of the pump, with a negative dynamic head on the suction side.

A section of a central heating system is shown in Fig. 34. It will be seen that the pump is positioned such that it can push the water through the pipework. This is known as a positive pressure system.

The water from the pump arrives at point A. Here, it has a choice of direction. For the system to work, the water needs to pass through the heating units. However, if the friction set up in the expansion pipe is less than that in the heating index circuit, the water will, instead, pass up the expansion pipe and into the feed and expansion tank. This will not overflow, because an equal volume of water is being drawn by the pump from the tank and through the boiler.

Under these conditions, the heating system will not work, but there are two ways in which matters can be corrected. Fig. 35 shows the same section, but here, the expansion pipe is separate from the heating circulation. Neither the expansion pipe nor the feed and expansion tank is now subject to the dynamic head produced by the pump, and the

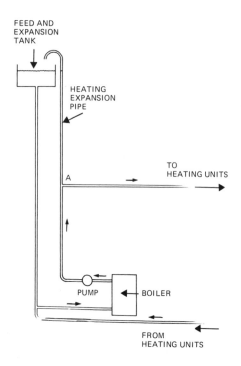

FEED AND
EXPANSION
TANK

HEATING
EXPANSION
PIPE

TO
HEATING UNITS

A

PUMP   BOILER

FROM
HEATING UNITS

Fig. 34   Section of a positive pressure central heating system.

only route which the water can follow is through the heating units.

The second alternative is the most common. This is to use a negative pressure system, which means that the pump now draws the water through the heating units. This is shown in Fig. 36.

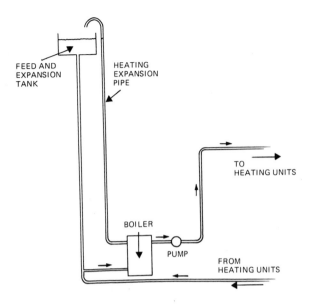

Fig. 35   Section of a modified positive pressure central heating system.

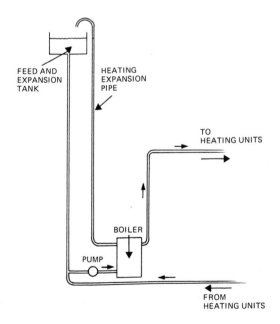

Fig. 36   Section of a negative pressure central heating system.

PRESSURE VESSELS FOR SEALED SYSTEMS

As explained in Chapter 3 (page 20), sealed systems do not have a feed and expansion tank. Instead, a pressure vessel is used to compensate for the changing volume of water, and to produce a static head. The principle is shown in Fig. 37.

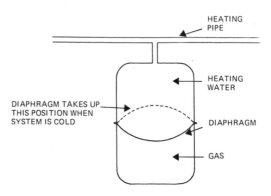

Fig. 37   Pressure vessel for use in a sealed system (shown with system hot).

The vessel consists of a closed container, the halves of which are separated by a flexible diaphragm. The part of the vessel above the diaphragm is connected to the heating pipework, and contains water. The lower part is filled with a gas, which may be either air or nitrogen. The pressure of the gas can be regulated.

When the heating system is cold, the water in the pipework is at its normal volume, that is, it takes up a normal amount of space. The pressure of the gas causes the diaphragm to take up a position as shown by the broken line.

The volume of water, as with most other substances, increases as the temperature is raised. The water thus requires a larger space. This is obtained by pushing the diaphragm downwards against the pressure of the gas.

It can thus be seen that the gas exerts a pressure on the water at all times. This pressure rises as the heating system warms up.

For sealed systems which are to operate at normal temperatures, the gas pressure is set so that the pressure exerted on the water is about the same as from a feed and expansion tank. The need for the tank, to supply the static head, is thus eliminated. In high temperature systems, the gas pressure is increased. This, in turn, exerts a greater pressure on the water. The water is thus prevented from boiling at the normal temperature of 212°F.

PRESSURE VESSEL SIZING

Pressure vessels are available in various sizes, and manufacturers supply data to enable the required model to be determined. A typical sizing table, based on the volume of water contained in the heating system, would be as follows:

Up to 10 gallons, a   4 litre vessel is required.
Up to 20 gallons, an   8 litre vessel is required.
Up to 31 gallons, a   12 litre vessel is required.
Up to 46 gallons, an 18 litre vessel is required.

In borderline cases, the next larger vessel should be selected.

In addition to the necessary safety devices, sealed systems need to be fitted with some method of topping-up the water. Automatic air bleed valves are also advisable. This is because the air contained in any bubbles in the water can be compressed more easily than the water, leading to a loss of system pressure. A similar effect is shown when air bubbles are present in the hydraulic braking system of a motor car.

II
JOINTS AND FITTINGS

In any pipework arrangement, a certain number of joints and fittings will be called for. These may be required to connect pipes together, or to join pipes up to other units, such as the boiler and pump.

Some years ago, pipes were manufactured in imperial sizes, the most common being ½in., ¾in. and 1in. diameter. These have now been replaced by metric sizes of 15mm., 22mm. and 28mm. diameter.

COMPRESSION JOINTS

These are the most expensive type, and are often used for pipe to pipe connections. Fig. 38 shows the assembly of a fitting for joining two pipes of equal size together.

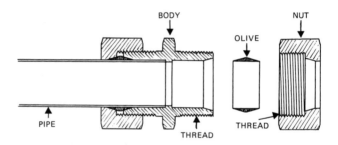

Fig. 38 Cross section of a compression fitting, for joining two pipes of equal size together.

The olive is a close fit on the outside diameter of the pipe. When the joint is assembled, the nut is tightened on to the thread. The conical shapes in the body and nut cause the olive to be compressed on to the pipe, thus making the joint. The body and nut are shaped such that a spanner or wrench can be used for tightening.

When buying compression fittings, a check should be made to ensure that the olives are not damaged, as sometimes happens. Fortunately, spare olives are available should an accident occur while fitting into the pipework.

Today, compression fittings are sold for metric size pipe only. If a connection to ¾in. pipe is required, a 22mm. fitting is bought, together with a special olive.

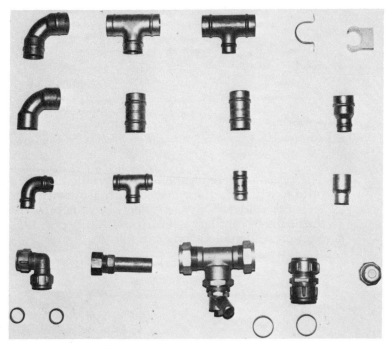

A selection of small-bore fittings of capillary and compression types.
Top to bottom, left to right:

22mm. *elbow*	*22mm.* *tee*	*22mm.–15mm.* *tee*	*pipe clips*
22mm. *elbow* *(nps)*	*22mm.–¾"* *convertor*	*22mm.* *straight*	*22mm.–15mm.* *reducer*
15mm. *elbow*	*15mm.* *tee*	*15mm.* *straight*	*22mm.–15mm.* *reducer (nps)*
15mm. *compression* *elbow*	*15mm.* *lead/copper* *adaptor*	*22mm.* *compression* *drain cock*	*22mm.* *straight* *connector*	*15mm.* *stop* *end*

In the case of ½in. and 15mm. sizes, compression fitting olives are interchangeable with each other. This is also true in the case of 1in. and 28mm. olives.

CAPILLARY JOINTS

These are much cheaper than compression fittings, and are used for similar purposes. There are two types:

   1. Presoldered, as shown in Fig. 39.

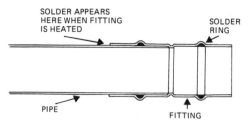

Fig. 39   Cross section of a presoldered capillary fitting, for joining two pipes of equal size.

The pipe ends are cleaned and assembled into the fitting, which is then heated with a blowlamp to melt the solder. This creeps between the pipe and the fitting by capillary action, thus making the joint.

2. Non-presoldered, as shown in Fig. 40.

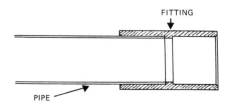

Fig. 40   Cross section of a non-presoldered capillary fitting for joining two pipes of equal size together.

This type of joint works exactly as before, but solder must be applied when the joint is heated.

Different people have their own preference for each. One advantage of type 1 is that, when heating, a ring of solder appears between the pipe and the fitting. This indicates that the solder has crept round the whole of the pipe, and a watertight joint should result.

Imperial and metric capillary fittings are not interchangeable with each other, and the correct size must always be selected. If it is necessary to connect imperial and metric pipes together, a special fitting with different size ends must be used.

Gas supply pipes to boilers and fires must always be constructed with capillary fittings.

It is possible to use capillary fittings with either copper or stainless steel pipe. However, soldering to stainless steel is not easy, and many tradesmen prefer to use compression fittings with this material.

THREADED JOINTS

Threaded joints are normally used to connect pipes into other equipment. They are available in imperial sizes with British Standard Pipe (B.S.P.) threads, and there are two types:

  I. With tapered threads, correctly known as B.S.T.P. threads.

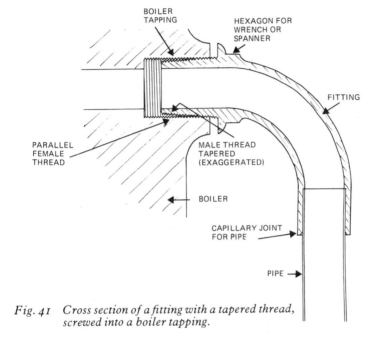

Fig. 41   Cross section of a fitting with a tapered thread, screwed into a boiler tapping.

Fig. 41 shows a fitting screwed into a boiler tapping. If the fitting is a bend or elbow, as shown, the opposite end must face a particular direction in order to line up with the pipe. If parallel threads were used, there would be little chance of the end facing the correct way when the fitting was tightened fully into the boiler. The use of a slow taper on the threads means that the fitting can be tightened into the boiler tapping, and then turned further to align the end with the pipe.

  In the type of fittings used in domestic central heating systems, the male thread is usually tapered, with the female thread parallel.

  2. With parallel threads (B.S.P.)

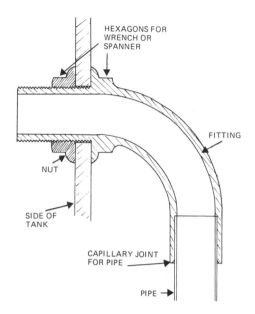

*Fig. 42   Cross section of a threaded fitting, being used to connect a pipe
into the side of a tank.*

A fitting in the side of a header tank is shown in
Fig. 42. This is secured by a nut, which means that it
is not necessary to rotate the fitting in order to
tighten the thread. Because the thickness of the side
of the tank is unknown to the fitting manufacturer,
the threads are both parallel. This enables the nut to
be tightened at any point along the male thread.
Compression and threaded joints can be disconnected
and reassembled any number of times without ill effects.
Because of this, thermostatic valves and control valves have
threaded or compression joints. Removal from the pipework for maintenance is thus made easy.
Disconnection and reassembly is possible with capillary
joints, but is rather more difficult because the pipe needs to
be pulled away at the same time as heat to melt the solder is
applied.
A wide range of fittings for every use is available, but the
actual joints will fall into one of the three main types shown
in this chapter. No problems should be encountered in
selecting the correct item for any application, as fitting
manufacturers and heating equipment merchants supply
illustrated lists.

12
TYPES OF HEATING SYSTEM

There are several different types of heating system. Apart from the boilers and heating units employed, the greatest differences are caused by the arrangement of the pipework used to connect the other parts together.

PUMPED PRIMARY SYSTEMS

All of the systems shown in Chapter 3 (pages 18 to 21) are of this type. The primary water, that is the water in the heating system, is moved through the coil inside the hot water cylinder by the action of the pump. The same pump is also used to move the water through the heating units. As explained in Chapter 3, a control valve is required to cut off the water flow to the heating units. This enables the system to be used for heating only the domestic hot water during warm weather.

The advantages of a pumped primary system are:

1. A faster warm-up of the domestic hot water can be achieved.
2. System temperatures can be controlled more closely.
3. 15mm. or 22mm. diameter pipework can be used to connect the boiler to the hot water cylinder. This avoids the use of larger diameter pipes which are not only more expensive than smaller ones, but are also much more difficult to bend.

The main disadvantage of pumped primary systems is that, for best operation, a rather complicated electrical control circuit is required. This is explained more fully in Chapter 13 (page 95).

The majority of systems being installed today are of this type.

GRAVITY PRIMARY SYSTEMS

A typical gravity primary system is shown in Fig. 43.

It can be seen that here, the primary water flow through the domestic hot water cylinder is not due to the action of the pump. Instead, the flow takes place by gravity. This makes use of the fact that when water is heated, it becomes lighter and moves upward, leaving the cooler water to sink. The pump is still used, but this is now employed only to move the water around the central heating system. When

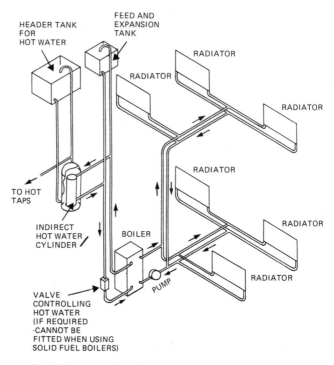

HEADER TANK FOR HOT WATER

FEED AND EXPANSION TANK

RADIATOR

RADIATOR

RADIATOR

TO HOT TAPS

RADIATOR

INDIRECT HOT WATER CYLINDER

BOILER

RADIATOR

PUMP

RADIATOR

VALVE CONTROLLING HOT WATER (IF REQUIRED -CANNOT BE FITTED WHEN USING SOLID FUEL BOILERS)

Fig. 43   Small bore gravity primary domestic hot water and central heating system.

the boiler is required to heat the domestic hot water in warm weather, the pump is switched off.

To assist the gravity circulation, large diameter pipes are required between the boiler and hot water cylinder.

This is the only type of system which can be used with solid fuel boilers. These are not so easily controlled as boilers burning other fuels, and an escape route for any excess heat must be provided. Because this escape route is through the hot water cylinder, devices to control the temperature of the domestic water cannot be fitted when firing with solid fuel.

DIVERTER SYSTEMS

This is a modified form of pumped primary system, and is shown in Fig. 44.

The control valve enables the pump to draw water either through the coil inside the domestic hot water cylinder, or through the central heating system, but not through both at

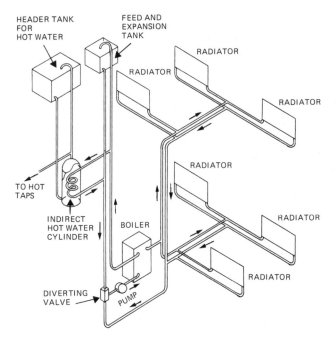

Fig. 44   Small bore diverter type domestic hot water and central heating system.

the same time. The output from the boiler is thus directed alternately to the two halves of the system, and a reduction in boiler size can be made.

This type of system suffers from two important disadvantages:

1. Because the boiler can pass heat to only one part of the system at a time, a priority must be selected. This can lead to one part of the system reaching the correct temperature, and the other remaining below the required level.
2. A somewhat complicated electrical control circuit is required to give the necessary priority selection. This is described in Chapter 13 (page 98).

The decision to install a diverter system to enable the boiler size to be reduced must be made with caution. Consider the building used for the calculations in Chapter 2:

Total heating load, less hot
water   36,503
15% allowance   5,475
                                            ―――――
                               41,978 B.Th.Us. per hr.

By using a diverter system, the boiler output required can be reduced from 53,478 B.Th.Us. per hour to 41,978 B.Th.Us. per hour. The extra cost of buying and operating the larger boiler must be balanced against the disadvantages of the system.

WALL MOUNTED GAS BOILERS

As explained in Chapter 4, some wall mounted gas boilers require a special pipework arrangement to prevent damage being caused to the boiler. This amounts to a modified form of pumped primary system, and is shown in Fig. 45.

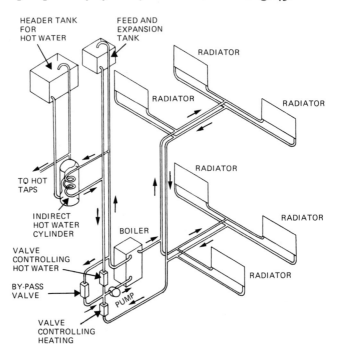

Fig. 45 Small bore pumped primary system, for some wall mounted gas boilers.

At certain times, the valves controlling the domestic hot water, and the central heating, will both be closed. To enable the pump to continue to pass water through the boiler, a bypass must be provided, as shown. This is fitted with a manual restricting valve.

The restricting valve is adjusted so that the bypass presents a greater resistance ot the water flow than either of the circulations through the heating system or the hot water cylinder. The bypass valve will thus allow water to pass only when both of the control valves are closed.

SYSTEMS CONTAINING RADIATORS AND FAN-CONVECTORS

It is possible to design a heating system containing radiators and fan-covectors. Likewise, skirting heaters can also be used instead of radiators. In either case, it is necessary to design the system so that the fan-convectors are fed with hot water throughout the whole of the time that the central heating is switched on. Installation is thus possible into either gravity or pumped primary systems, but not into diverter systems.

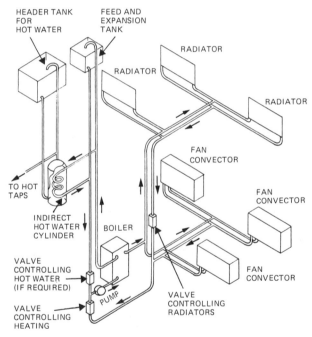

Fig. 46   Small bore pumped primary system, with radiators and fan convectors.

Fig. 46 shows a pumped primary system with three radiators and three fan-convectors. It can be seen that if the valve controlling the radiators is turned off, water can still circulate through the fan convectors. Another valve is provided to shut down the whole of the heating system when required.

SINGLE PIPE CIRCULATION

Before fan convectors and skirting heaters came into use for domestic heating installations, radiators were used. These were often installed as shown in Fig. 47, and this is known as a single pipe circulation.

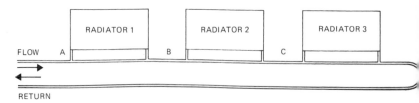

Fig. 47   Single pipe circulation.

Ignoring any heat loss through pipework emission, the temperature of the water at A will be about the same as that set on the boiler thermostat. At B, the water temperature will have dropped somewhat. This is because some of the water will have passed through radiator 1, and will have lost some heat there. Likewise, the temperature of the water at C will be lower than that at B. The last radiator in the system will thus be fed with water which is at a much lower temperature than at the start.

The problem is easily overcome by installing a twin pipe circulation, and for this reason, single pipe systems are now almost obsolete.

TWIN PIPE CIRCULATION

A twin pipe circulation system containing three radiators is shown in Fig. 48.

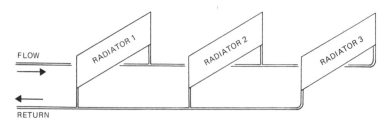

Fig. 48   Twin pipe circulation.

It will be seen that now, each radiator receives water at boiler temperature (ignoring pipework emission). A greater length of pipe is required, but this greatly outweighs the disadvantage of single pipe circulation. When using fan-convectors, it is even more important to use the twin pipe method.

LOOP CIRCULATION

For systems where skirting heaters are used throughout, it is sometimes convenient to use a loop circulation. Fig. 49 shows a double loop circulation in a two-storey building.

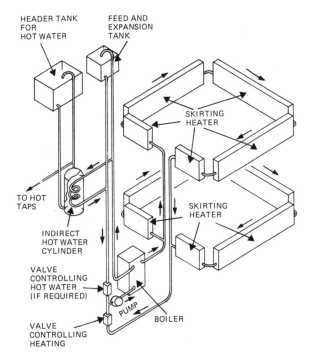

Fig. 49   Small bore pumped primary system, with skirting heaters arranged in loops.

As with single pipe circulation, the temperature of the water falls as it passes through the heaters. The length of each heater must be increased to account for this, and the calculation is carried out as follows.

Suppose that three skirting heaters form a loop. These are required to give an emission of 7,000 B.Th.Us. per hour, 8,000 B.Th.Us. per hour and 5,000 B.Th.Us. per hour with an average boiler flow temperature of 180°F. How long must each heater be if the water temperature drop through the whole of the loop is 20°F? The arrangement is shown in Fig. 50.

FLOW   A   B   C   D

7,000 B.Th.Us. PER HOUR   8,000 B.Th.Us. PER HOUR   5,000 B.Th.Us. PER HOUR   RETURN

Fig. 50   Skirting heaters in loop circulation.

Total heat load from A to D is 7,000 + 8,000 + 5,000
$$= 20,000 \, \text{B.Th.Us. per hr.}$$
Temperature drop from A to D is 20°F.

One pound of water gives out one B.Th.U. when allowed to cool through 1°F.

Therefore one pound of water gives out 20 B.Th.Us. when allowed to cool through 20°F.

Therefore the weight of water required to pass every hour is
$$20,000 \div 20$$
$$= 1,000 \, \text{pounds.}$$
Average water temperature at A is 180°F.

Heat load in section AB is 7,000 B.Th.Us. per hour.

Therefore the temperature lost by the water in passing through AB is
$$7,000 \div 1,000$$
$$= 7°F.$$
Therefore the average water temperature at B is
$$180 - 7$$
$$= 173°F.$$
Likewise, it can be shown that the average water temperature at C will be 165°F, and at D, 160°F.

The skirting heaters can now be sized by using manufacturer's tables, similar to the method shown in Chapter 7 (page 56). However, it is now necessary to use the average flow temperature of 173°F for section BC, and 165°F for section CD.

For the circulation shown, the total heat load is 20,000 B.Th.Us. per hour. Skirting heaters with an element pipe of 22mm. diameter will be required for this. (See Chapter 8, page 61).

It should be noted that, with loop circulation, individual heaters cannot be turned off. However, some degree of room temperature control can be achieved by adjustment of each heater damper (page 55).

13
CONTROL CIRCUITS

Control circuits for central heating systems is a subject in itself, and impossible to cover fully in one chapter. It is intended here to give only a basic outline of the principles involved, together with some specimen circuits. Those wishing to study the subject further should read my book 'Do Your Own Central Heating Controls', published by W. Foulsham & Co. Ltd.

Control circuits consist of several main items which are connected together in various ways to give the required operation.

TIME SWITCHES

As the name suggests, time switches are devices which are able to switch a power supply on or off under the control of a clock. Various switching arrangements are available.

PROGRAMMERS

Programmers are similar to time switches, and are used for similar purposes. Internally, they are more complicated, and are able to provide a wider range of automatic sequences than are available from time switches.

Only by using a time switch or programmer can fully automatic running of the heating system be achieved. Uses include:

1. Switching the system on in the morning. Rooms are thus warmed prior to getting out of bed. The only other method of achieving this is to run the system throughout the night, which is wasteful.
2. If the building is left empty during the day, the rooms can likewise be warmed prior to anyone arriving home in the evening.
3. Automatic switching off of the system can be achieved when going to bed at night, or leaving home in the morning.

ROOM THERMOSTATS

The occupants of a room are interested in the air temperature, and not the temperature of the radiators and pipework. Room thermostats are thus used to monitor room air temperature, and control the heating system as required.

Most installations today use one room thermostat to control the whole of the system. This is a compromise which, with correct balancing of the heating units, can work fairly well. It is possible to position a thermostat in each room, but the resulting circuitry becomes very complicated.

HOT WATER CYLINDER THERMOSTATS

In order to give electrical control of the domestic hot water temperature, a hot water cylinder thermostat is used. This is secured to the outside of the cylinder by a strap which passes around the circumference. Because the thermostat is held in close contact with the cylinder, the temperature of the water inside is monitored.

MOTORIZED VALVES

These are control valves which are positioned in pipes. In response to electrical signals, they are able either to allow or stop the flow of water through a pipe, or to divert its course.

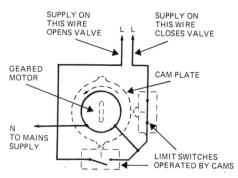

Fig. 51   Actuator for on/off motorized valve (shown in open position).

Fig. 51 shows an on/off motorized valve when the left-hand supply wire is energized. Under these conditions, the valve is open, thus allowing water to flow through the pipe. If the valve is now required to close, the power supply must be switched to the right-hand wire. Current will flow through the closed right-hand limit switch, and cause the motor to run. After about one minute, the valve will become fully closed, as shown in Fig. 52.

Switching the power supply on to the left-hand wire will again cause the valve to open.

Motorized diverting valves are similar. Here, a power supply on the left-hand wire will always allow water to pass through the valve via one route. Passage through a second route can be allowed by energizing the right-hand wire instead.

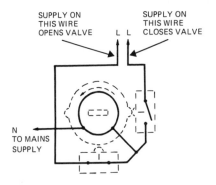

Fig. 52   Actuator for on/off motorized valve (shown in closed position).

RELAYS

In central heating applications, relays are required only in the more complicated control circuits, and examples will be found later in this chapter. As the name suggests, they are used to relay electrical power from one part of a circuit to another.

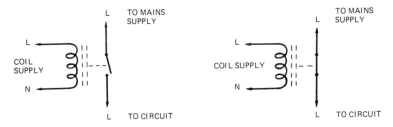

Fig. 53 (a)   Relay with coil de-energized (normal position).   *Fig. 53 (b)   Relay with coil energized, and output to circuit live.*

Fig. 53(a) shows the electrical diagram of a relay with the coil de-energized. This is known as the normal position, and the switch is held open by a spring. The circuit being controlled by the switch is thus de-energized.

If power is now applied to the coil, a magnetic field is set up. This overcomes the tension in the spring, and causes the switch to close, as shown in Fig. 53(b). Current is now able to pass through the switch, and to the circuit being controlled.

When the coil is again de-energized, the condition shown in Fig. 53(a) will result.

The design and operation of the control circuit depends greatly on the type of heating system, and specimen circuits follow for each type. It must be emphasized that these have been chosen to illustrate the principles involved only, and that either simpler or more complicated arrangements can be used.

GRAVITY PRIMARY SYSTEMS WITH SOLID FUEL BOILERS (Fig. 43, page 84)

As explained in Chapters 4 and 12, solid fuel boilers must be equipped with an escape route for the dispersal of excess heat. This is usually via the domestic hot water cylinder, which cannot be fitted with any device which cuts off the water flow.

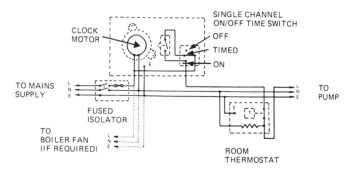

Fig. 54   *Control circuit for a gravity primary system, with solid fuel boiler.*

Fig. 54 shows a suitable circuit. A time switch is included to give a simple form of automatic control. The central heating pump is controlled by the room thermostat, and is switched on or off as required.

The whole circuit is shown as being controlled by a fused isolator. This is a double pole switch, one pole controlling the live supply, and the other, the neutral. A fuse, usually of the cartridge type, is positioned in the live conductor.

Because it is designed for use with a solid fuel boiler, the circuit is not connected to the boiler in any way. This means that domestic hot water will be available whenever the boiler is alight, and the circuit will control only the heating system.

For solid fuel boilers which are fan assisted, the power supply to the boiler can be taken directly from the fused isolator, as shown by the dotted lines.

GRAVITY PRIMARY SYSTEMS WITH OIL OR GAS BOILERS (Fig. 43, page 84)

When using boilers which can be controlled more easily, such as oil or gas fired types, an escape route for excess heat is not required. It is necessary, though, to arrange the circuit to control the boiler, and this is shown in Fig. 55.

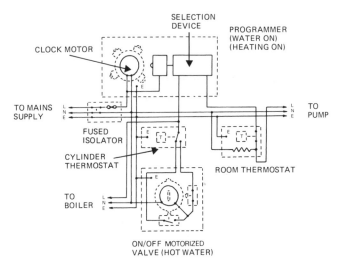

Fig. 55   Circuit for a gravity primary system, with an oil or gas boiler.

The boiler will be energized whenever the programmer dictates that the domestic water is switched on. This does not mean that the boiler will run continuously, because its internal thermostat will cause it to start up and shut down as required.

Temperature control of the domestic hot water is achieved by the use of a cylinder thermostat and motorized valve. When the water temperature is lower than that required, as shown, the thermostat causes the valve to open. On reaching the specified temperature, the thermostat switches the power to the right-hand valve supply wire, and the valve closes.

When the central heating is switched on at the programmer, the pump is controlled by the room thermostat.

PUMPED PRIMARY SYSTEMS (Figs. 3, 4, 5 and 6, pages 18 to 21)

In pumped primary systems, the pump not only moves water around the central heating system, but through the coil in the domestic hot water cylinder also. Thus, the pump must run whenever the boiler is energized, and room temperature control by pump switching is no longer possible.

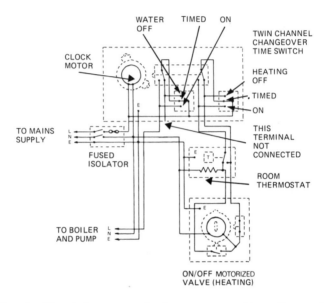

Fig. 56   Circuit for a pumped primary system, with an oil or gas boiler.

Fig. 56 shows a circuit which is designed to give room temperature control only. This is achieved by the use of a room thermostat and motorized valve. When the heating is switched off at the time switch, the current to close the valve bypasses the thermostat.

The fused isolator is very important in this type of circuit. This is because most circuits using motorized valves contain live parts, even when the time switch is in the OFF position.

There is no temperature control of the domestic hot water, other than from the boiler thermostat. The boiler and pump are both energized as long as the domestic water is switched on at the time switch.

The circuit in Fig. 56 can be adapted to give control of the domestic hot water temperature, by the addition of a cylinder thermostat and second motorized valve. This is shown in Fig. 57.

The circuit includes an interesting additional feature. The boiler and pump are controlled by auxiliary switches on

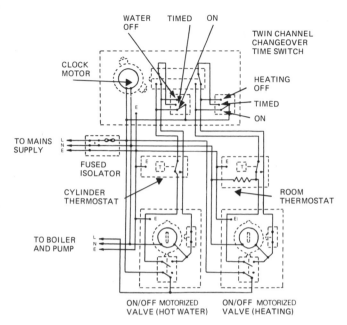

WATER TIMED ON
OFF

TWIN CHANNEL
CHANGEOVER
TIME SWITCH

CLOCK
MOTOR

HEATING
OFF

TIMED

ON

TO MAINS
SUPPLY

FUSED
ISOLATOR

CYLINDER
THERMOSTAT

ROOM
THERMOSTAT

TO BOILER
AND PUMP

ON/OFF MOTORIZED
VALVE (HOT WATER)

ON/OFF MOTORIZED
VALVE (HEATING)

*Fig. 57   Control circuit for a pumped primary system, with temperature
control of the domestic hot water.*

the motorized valves. When either or both valves are open, power can pass to the boiler and pump. When both valves are closed, the boiler and pump are de-energized. This not only saves fuel, but also ensures that the pump does not attempt to move water round the system when both motorized valves are closed.

PUMPED PRIMARY SYSTEMS WITH WALL MOUNTED GAS BOILERS (Fig. 45, page 86)

For some models of wall mounted gas boilers, it is necessary for the pump to continue running after the boiler has shut off. This is to disperse heat from the boiler which would otherwise cause damage. The circuit in Fig. 58 is arranged to do this, and a bypass in the pipework, for use when both control valves are closed, will be required.

The pump is controlled via a timing relay. This is a relay which, when the coil is de-energized, does not release the switch immediately. The length of time delay is adjustable, and would be set to ensure that all the heat had been removed from the boiler before the switch opens.

The circuit is shown just after the control valves have closed. The boiler is de-energized, but the pump is still

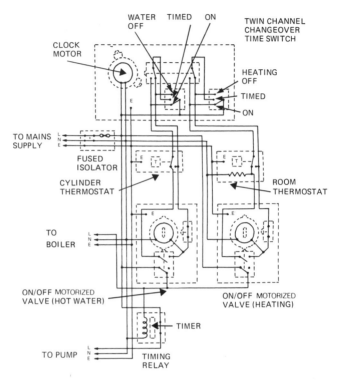

Fig. 58   Circuit for a pumped primary system, used with some wall mounted gas boilers.

running. With this circuit, the only way of de-energizing the boiler and pump together, and thus risk damage, would be to open the fused isolator when the boiler was running.

DIVERTER SYSTEMS (Fig. 44, page 85)

For the automatic operation of the priority selection in a diverter system, a cylinder thermostat and a room thermostat are required. These are arranged as shown in Fig. 59.

When the priority switch is set to WATER, the heating system will receive heat from the boiler only when the water temperature is up to that set on the cylinder thermostat. Likewise, when the priority switch is set to HEATING, the domestic water will be warmed only when the rooms are at the required temperature.

Diverter systems use a modified form of motorized valve. Instead of giving an on/off operation, the diverting valve causes the route taken by the water to be changed.

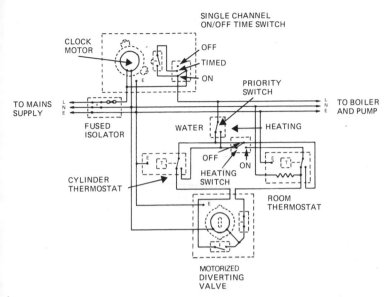

Fig. 59   Control circuit for a diverter system.

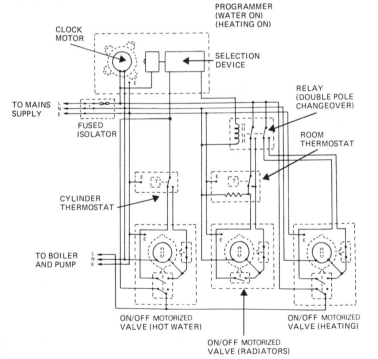

Fig. 60   Circuit for a pumped primary system, with radiators and fan convectors.

99

SYSTEMS WITH RADIATORS AND
FAN-CONVECTORS (Fig. 46, page 87)

As explained in Chapter 12 (page 87), a special circuit is necessary to control heating systems containing radiators and fan convectors. This is shown in Fig. 60.

Whenever the heating is switched on, the boiler and pump are energized, and the valve controlling the heating is open. This ensures that, during heating periods, the fan convectors are fed constantly with hot water. Room temperature control in these areas is from the internal thermostats in the convectors.

On the other hand, the areas heated by radiators are under the control of a room thermostat and a motorized valve. The valve will control the flow of water through the radiators, and thus maintain the required room air temperature.

The relay shown in this circuit is noteworthy. This is of the double pole changeover type, each pole controlling a motorized valve. This is the only method by which some types of valve can be connected so that two operate together.

Fan-convectors require their own power supply to operate the fan. This can be taken from a convenient wall socket, and is not shown in Fig. 60.

14
DESIGNING THE INSTALLATION

Because buildings, heating systems and personal requirements vary so much, it is not possible to lay down exactly how any particular installation should be designed. It is hoped that the previous chapters in this book have given enough information about component parts, and how they may be connected together to form a complete installation.

It is suggested that, in designing a system, the order of working is basically as shown in this book. This is detailed below, together with various notes and reminders.

CALCULATE THE HEATING LOAD
(Chapters 1 and 2)

Calculate the heat loss from each area in turn, using the table of U-values for each part of the structure.

DECIDE SIZE AND POSITION OF DOMESTIC HOT WATER CYLINDER (Chapters 2 and 5)

Usually, a capacity of 30 gallons is adequate for the average family, but this can be altered, if required. Decide which model of cylinder is to be used, and note the external dimensions.

When the position is decided, the cylinder can be marked in on the building plan, such as Fig. 2 (page 12).

DECIDE WHICH FUEL IS TO BE USED
(Chapter 4)

Solid fuel — boilers cannot be closely controlled, and need more attention than other types.
— area required for fuel storage.
Gas — fully automatic control.
— no fuel storage required.
— fuel supplies not so easily cut off by strikes.
Oil — fully automatic control.
— fuel tank required, with easy access.

The cost of fuel and boilers may also have a bearing on the choice of fuel to be used. A more expensive boiler is a once-only cost. A fuel which remains more expensive than others carries a continuous penalty.

DECIDE BOILER SITING AND TYPE OF FLUE (Chapter 4)

Solid fuel — conventional flue required.

— free standing and room heater types.

Gas — large range of conventional and balanced flue models.

— wall mounted types have small overall size.

Oil— mainly conventional flue, but some balanced flue models available.

Remember that only balanced flue boilers are safe for installation in garages.

DECIDE ON TYPE OF SYSTEM
(Chapters 3 and 12)

Small bore.

Microbore — with or without manifolds.

Sealed system. This is no advantage unless:
  — high water temperatures are required.
  — the feed and expansion tank cannot be sited high enough. This problem can sometimes be overcome by use of a self-priming hot water cylinder.

Gravity primary — must be used with solid fuel boilers.
  — large diameter pipework is required between the boiler and hot water cylinder.

Pumped primary — advisable when the domestic hot water cylinder is well away from the boiler.
  — close control of the domestic hot water temperature can be achieved.

Diverter system — doubtful whether savings obtained are worth the inconveniences of priority operation.

DECIDE ON BOILER TO BE USED
(Chapters 2 and 4)

Decide on the reheat period for the domestic hot water, and thus calculate the heat requirements. Apply the boiler allowance to determine the boiler output required.

Consult price lists and brochures to decide on the boiler to be used. Note the external dimensions, and mark in on the building plan.

DECIDE ON TYPE OF HEATING UNITS
(Chapters 6 and 7)

Radiators cannot be used with high temperature systems, and sometimes interfere with the positioning of furniture.

Skirting heaters can distribute heat over a large area by convection.

Fan-convectors are rather more complicated and expensive than other types of heating unit. They are not completely silent in operation, but their heat emission is high for their size.

DECIDE SIZE AND POSITION OF HEATING UNITS (Chapters 6 and 7)

The heat loss from each area is known from the calculations shown in Chapters 1 and 2. The heating units must be capable of making good each of these losses.

The area in which the boiler is sited will receive a certain amount of heat due to boiler emission.

When the physical size of each heating unit is known, their positions can be decided. Long, narrow rooms will be best heated by positioning a heating unit near to each end.

The position of each unit should be marked in on the building plan.

DECIDE ON PIPEWORK ARRANGEMENT FOR THE HEATING UNITS (Chapter 12)

Single pipe circulation is now practically obsolete, and it is far better to use the twin pipe method.

Skirting heaters can be piped into the form of a loop, but control is not as flexible as with individual pipes.

Fan-convectors require special arrangements so that the supply of hot water to them cannot be interrupted during periods when the heating system is switched on.

DECIDE ON THE POSITION OF THE HEADER TANKS

Decide on a position for the domestic water header tank. Where an attic is available, this is usually the position chosen. Arrangements must be made to protect the tank and pipes from frost.

When a feed and expansion tank is required for the heating system, it is usual to choose a position adjacent to the domestic header tank.

Mark the positions on the building plan.

DECIDE ON THE POSITION OF THE PUMP

Where the pump is not contained inside the boiler casing, a separate position must be found. This should be marked on the building plan.

DECIDE ON THE POSITION OF THE PIPE RUNS

The route to be taken by each pipe must now be decided, and the runs marked on the building plan. Any manifolds to be used with microbore systems should also be positioned and marked at this stage. Points to consider are as follows:

1. In a building with floors constructed of wooden boards on joists, it is easy to position the pipes below the floorboards. Connections to the heating units will then project upward. Any air in the system will rise to the top of the heating units, where it can be bled off easily. Such an arrangement is shown in Fig. 61.

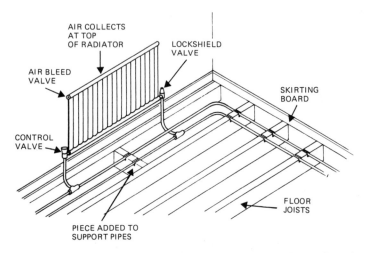

Fig. 61   A radiator connected to underfloor small bore pipework (twin pipe circulation — floorboards not shown).

When using this arrangement, it is important to ensure that two pipes do not cross on a joist. If this did occur, it would be necessary to cut a deep slot in the joist, which would cause weakness.

2. After buildings have been erected with solid floors, it is very difficult to instal pipework below them. The usual method here is to position the flow and return pipes above the ceiling, with a drop to each heating unit. Unfortunately, air will now become trapped in the flow and return pipes, and some method of bleeding this off must be provided. Fig. 62 shows a suitable arrangement.

The pipes are simply laid on the ceiling joists, and are not slotted in. By placing packing pieces between the joists and pipe, a gradual slope can be produced. This will encourage trapped air to collect

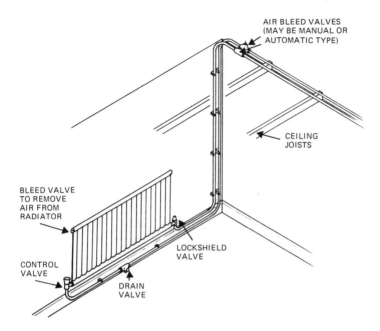

AIR BLEED VALVES
(MAY BE MANUAL OR
AUTOMATIC TYPE)

CEILING
JOISTS

BLEED VALVE
TO REMOVE
AIR FROM
RADIATOR

LOCKSHIELD
VALVE

CONTROL
VALVE

DRAIN
VALVE

*Fig. 62   A radiator connected to overhead small bore pipework (twin
pipe circulation — ceiling not shown).*

at the highest point, and bleed valves should be positioned there.

3. In multi-storey buildings with solid ground floors, a combination of 1 and 2 can be used for heating units on the ground floor. It is not now necessary to position bleed valves in the horizontal flow and return pipes, because air will find its way to the top of the first-floor heating units.

DECIDE SIZE AND POSITION OF PRESSURE VESSEL (Chapter 10)

For sealed systems, the size of the pressure vessel required must now be determined.

The position should also now be decided, and marked on the building plan. The vessel is often fitted near to the boiler.

The building plan now shows the position of each component in the system, and for the building in Chapter 2, would be as shown in Fig. 63.

The main drawback with this type of plan is that pipes which are vertically above each other cannot easily be

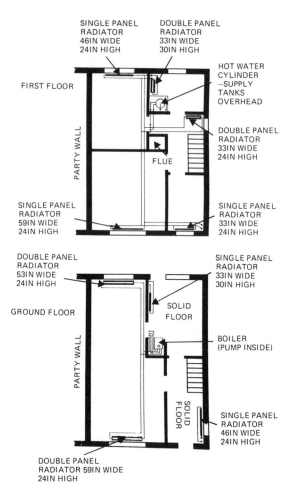

SINGLE PANEL RADIATOR 46IN WIDE 24IN HIGH

DOUBLE PANEL RADIATOR 33IN WIDE 30IN HIGH

FIRST FLOOR

HOT WATER CYLINDER —SUPPLY TANKS OVERHEAD

PARTY WALL

DOUBLE PANEL RADIATOR 33IN WIDE 24IN HIGH

FLUE

SINGLE PANEL RADIATOR 59IN WIDE 24IN HIGH

SINGLE PANEL RADIATOR 33IN WIDE 24IN HIGH

DOUBLE PANEL RADIATOR 53IN WIDE 24IN HIGH

SINGLE PANEL RADIATOR 33IN WIDE 30IN HIGH

GROUND FLOOR

SOLID FLOOR

PARTY WALL

BOILER (PUMP INSIDE)

SOLID FLOOR

SINGLE PANEL RADIATOR 46IN WIDE 24IN HIGH

DOUBLE PANEL RADIATOR 59IN WIDE 24IN HIGH

Fig. 63   Building plan, showing the position of each item.

shown. An example of this is to be seen around the boiler.
For this reason, some designers prefer to use an isometric
type of drawing, as shown in Fig. 64. Here, pipes can be
shown more clearly, but the drawing can easily become a
confused mass of lines.

CALCULATE PIPE SIZES (Chapter 8)

The building plan now includes all of the information
required to calculate the pipe sizes.

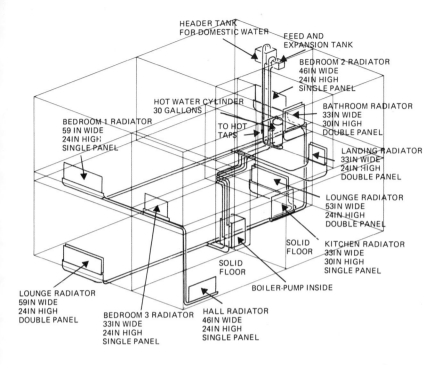

HEADER TANK
FOR DOMESTIC WATER
FEED AND
EXPANSION TANK

BEDROOM 2 RADIATOR
46IN WIDE
24IN HIGH
SINGLE PANEL

HOT WATER CYLINDER
30 GALLONS

BATHROOM RADIATOR
33IN WIDE
30IN HIGH
DOUBLE PANEL

BEDROOM 1 RADIATOR
59 IN WIDE
24IN HIGH
SINGLE PANEL

TO HOT
TAPS

LANDING RADIATOR
33IN WIDE
24IN HIGH
DOUBLE PANEL

LOUNGE RADIATOR
53IN WIDE
24IN HIGH
DOUBLE PANEL

SOLID
FLOOR

KITCHEN RADIATOR
33IN WIDE
30IN HIGH
SINGLE PANEL

SOLID
FLOOR

BOILER-PUMP INSIDE

LOUNGE RADIATOR
59IN WIDE
24IN HIGH
DOUBLE PANEL

BEDROOM 3 RADIATOR
33IN WIDE
24IN HIGH
SINGLE PANEL

HALL RADIATOR
46IN WIDE
24IN HIGH
SINGLE PANEL

*Fig. 64   Isometric drawing of a building, showing the position of each
item. Compare this with Fig. 63.*

After calculation, the sizes can be marked on the plan, or
different colours can be used to indicate the various
diameters.

The total length of each size of pipe can now be found.

SELECT PUMP (Chapter 9)

If a range of pumps is available, a suitable one must be
selected. If there is no choice, a check can still be made to
ensure that the pump in question is adequate. The pump
setting required can also be found at this stage.

SELECT JOINTS AND FITTINGS (Chapter 11)

Compression — expensive, but easy to fit into copper or
   stainless steel pipe.
   — can easily be dismantled and reassembled.
Capillary — not easy to make a satisfactory joint with
   stainless steel pipe.

Each part of the system must now be considered carefully, and the required fittings decided upon. A large scale sketch of the more complicated sections is sometimes helpful here. Care must be taken not to overlook items such as bleed valves and drain taps.

Some thought must also be given now to the method of installation. Consider Fig. 65.

(a) ELBOW   (b) SWEEP BEND   (c) BENT PIPE WITH STRAIGHT CONNECTOR

Fig. 65   Three methods of changing the direction of a small bore pipe.

Where space is not restricted, (a) is unsuitable, because sharp bends cause increased friction to be set up against the flow of water. The larger radius bends in (b) and (c) are preferable. The straight connector in (c) may not be required, depending on the shape of the pipe, and any space restrictions. Even if a connector is required, (c) is likely to be the cheapest, but more pipe bending will need to be carried out.

A list of all the fittings required can now be compiled.

DECIDE ON THE CONTROLS
(Chapters 5, 6 and 13)

Control of the domestic hot water temperature at a low level is not possible with solid fuel boilers. Mechanical or electrical methods can be used with oil or gas boilers.

Control of room air temperature by individual mechanical radiator thermostats, or by electrical methods, is possible.

Some electrical circuits can be arranged to switch off the boiler when the required temperatures are reached. This saves fuel.

Fan-convectors, and some wall mounted gas boilers need special arrangements.

The positioning of the various items of control equipment in the pipework must not be overlooked. these can be marked on the building plan.

A list of the items of control equipment required can now be made.

15
COMMON OPERATIONS

Whatever type of heating system is being installed, the method of carrying out several operations must be grasped. These will be dealt with in turn.

PIPE CUTTING

Pipe can be cut by either of two methods:
1. Using a hacksaw, the pipe being held in a vice. It is important that the cut is made as squarely as possible across the pipe. There are two methods of marking the line along which to cut, and these are shown in Fig. 66.

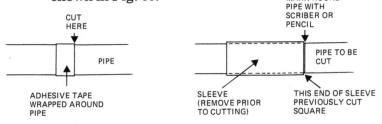

Fig. 66   Two methods of marking a pipe, prior to cutting with a hacksaw.

The hacksaw blade should be as fine as possible to give the best cutting conditions.
2. Using a special pipe cutter, as shown in Fig. 67.

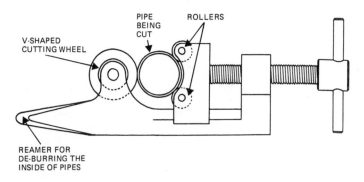

Fig. 67   A pipe cutter.

A pipe-bender of this type, set up to bend 15mm. pipe, can be hired for the job.

Cutting with a pipe-cutter, the pipe being securely held in the vice fitment of the bender.

The pipe having been cut to length, the cut end is reamed clean with the pipe-cutter.

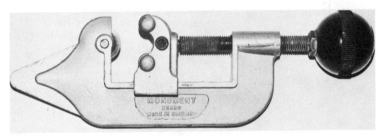

A commercial pipe-cutter, showing clearly the cutting wheel and integral reamer.

The pipe does not need to be held in a vice, and a square cut is guaranteed by the arrangement of the rollers. The pressure on the screw causes the cutting wheel to bite into the surface of the pipe. The whole cutter is rotated, the pipe being held stationary. By adjusting the pressure on the screw, the cutting wheel is moved inward by an amount equal to the wall thickness of the pipe.

When using this method, care must be taken not to force the cutting wheel into the work too fast. The wheel must also be kept sharp. The result of neglecting either of these points is shown in Fig. 68. This is undesirable, as the water flow will be restricted.

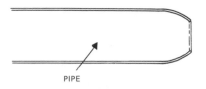

PIPE

Fig. 68   *Pipe end deformed by incorrect use (or maintenance) of the pipe cutter.*

Having plumbed a vertical line on the wall each radiator bracket is securely screwed in place at the estimated height.

PIPE CLEANING

Whenever a pipe has been cut, all burrs and sharp edges must be removed from the cut end, using a fine tooth file. The inside and outside diameters of the pipe are particularly important. Many pipe cutters incorporate a reamer for cleaning off internal burrs.

Before being fitted into the system, the inside of all pipes must be as clean as possible. Loose matter can be shaken or blown out of bent pipes. Straight lengths of small bore pipe can be cleaned by pushing through a piece of rag with a wooden lath.

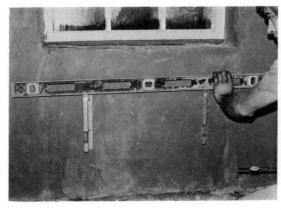

With both brackets in place it is as well to check their level before hanging the radiator.

Right: A typical radiator bracket in position. Some vertical adjustment is possible with the slotted hole.

BENDING SMALL BORE PIPE

When bending any thin wall pipe, the danger is that it will flatten or kink at the point of bend. For this reason, a bending spring is used. This allows the pipe to be bent, but does not allow it to flatten. After producing the bend, the spring is turned anticlockwise and pulled out. A length of stiff wire is attached to the spring when the bend is some distance from the end of the pipe.

After inserting the appropriate spring, copper pipe up to 22mm. diameter, and stainless steel pipe up to 15mm. diameter can be bent over the knee. Larger diameters will require a bending machine, which can usually be hired for a few pounds from a tool hire shop. If hiring, plan the work so that the machine will be required for as short a time as possible. Also tell the shop what pipe diameters are to be bent so that the correct equipment can be provided.

Whatever method is used, it is best to bend the pipe slightly too much, and then pull it back to the required shape. This tends to make it easier to free the bending spring.

In some situations, pipes are best bent before being cut to length. Consider the position shown in Fig. 69, where a pipe is to be made to connect two previously placed fittings A and B.

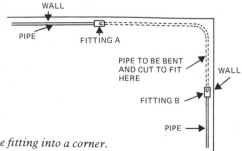

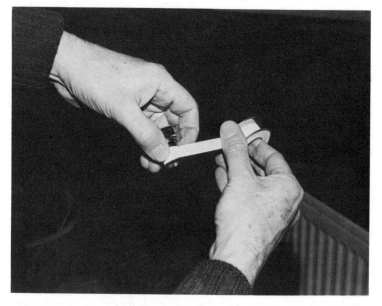

Fig. 69   Pipe fitting into a corner.

Ptfe tape is a clean and easy way of producing a water-tight joint — in this case between valve and radiator.

Starting from A, it will be very difficult to position the bend exactly as required. An error of more than about ½in. will either render the pipe useless, or lead to an untidy installation.

The safest method is to measure the distance from A to the bend, and add 3in. The bend is produced, and the pipe is

The valve is fitted into the radiator using a hexagon wrench, a job made easier if the radiator end is raised on a piece of timber.

The valve body must be well tightened, which means using a spanner of adequate size and snug fit.

laid as near to its final position as possible. Marks are made on the pipe showing the positions of A and B, and the pipe is cut in these two places. A perfect fit is thus guaranteed for the cost of a few inches of pipe.

When cutting a pipe which is to mate with a fitting, remember that a short length of pipe is required to enter the fitting.

With the radiator hung and ready to receive the pipework, this job required a dividing wall to be drilled next.

The previously bent and cut pipe is now connected up to the radiator.

BENDING MICROBORE PIPE

Relatively speaking, microbore pipe is nowhere near as thin walled as small bore pipe, and a bending spring is not required. Bends can be produced by either of two methods:

1. By hand. The pipe is gripped in each hand, and carefully bent using the thumbs. Bends which will be out of sight should be made with as large a radius as possible, to reduce water friction to a minimum.
2. By using a special pipe bender, which is operated by one hand, similar to a pair of pliers. The resulting bend is very neat, but confined to a radius of about 2in.

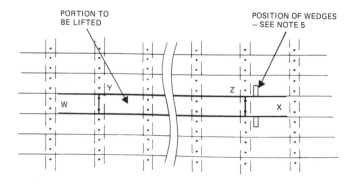

Fig. 70 Method of lifting tongued and grooved floorboards.

LIFTING FLOORBOARDS

Many wooden floors are constructed with tongued and grooved boards. Each board is thus interlocked with its neighbours, and cannot be lifted separately.

The easiest method of lifting a single board is to cut the tongues with a saw. Chiselling is not to be recommended, as it tends to cause too much damage.

The procedure is shown in Fig. 70. Suppose that the shaded board Y–Z needs to be lifted.

Because the floor shown here is to be screeded over, the next step is to protect the pipe with anti-corrosion wrap.

This photograph clearly shows the cut tongue of the tongued-and-grooved floorboard and the joists cut just enough to accommodate the pipework.

1. The tongue on each board is cut by making two sawcuts between some points W and X. Special hand saws with curved blades are available for this, or ordinary tenon saws can be used. Where nails are not likely to be encountered, a portable electric circular saw will be quickest. The blade should be set so that the depth of cut is not greater than the thickness of the floorboards.

2. The nails securing the board between W and X should, if possible, be removed. Alternatively, the heads can be punched right through and into the joists.

3. Using the position of the nails in adjacent joists, mark each end of the section to be removed. These marks should lie about halfway across the joists, and are shown at Y and Z.

4. If the length of board between Y and Z is not continuous, move on to 5.

    If the length is continuous, the board must be cut through on either of the marks, in this case, Y. If available, the special curved blade saw can be used for this, or a chisel. A portable electric circular saw can also be used, but great care must be taken to avoid nails.

    With either sawing method, the board on each side of the one being removed will be partially cut into. Nail removal as in 3 will be required in these areas.

5. Working from the cut end, the board now needs to be lifted. This is done progressively, using a floorboard bolster, and eventually, two wedges are inserted between Z and X. This has the effect of lifting the board at Z above the level of the surrounding floor.

6. The board is cut at Z.

When the board above a heating pipe is replaced, it should be secured with screws. This enables it to be lifted easily at a later date.

SMALL BORE PIPES IN JOISTS

It is often necessary to run a pipe through a joist, and a typical case would be as shown in Fig. 61 (page 104). The arrangement is shown more clearly in Fig. 71.

A slot is cut in the joist which is ½in. wider, and ¼in. deeper than the outside diameter of the pipe. When the covering floorboard is refitted, the space between the pipe

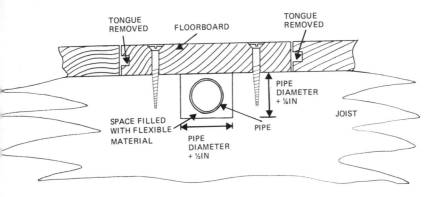

FLOORBOARD

PIPE
DIAMETER
+ ¼IN

JOIST

SPACE FILLED
WITH FLEXIBLE
MATERIAL

PIPE
DIAMETER
+ ½IN

PIPE

Fig. 71   Method of passing small bore pipes through joists.

and the slot is filled with a flexible material, such as foam rubber. This steadies the pipe, but allows a small amount of movement. Some movement is inevitable due to expansion of the pipe. If the foam rubber is not fitted, the pipe may make a noise as it moves over the wood.

Where the pipe runs parallel with the joists, pieces of wood should be fitted to act as supports. One of these is shown in Fig. 61, and the number required is as follows:

For 15mm. diameter pipe — every 4ft.
For 22mm. diameter pipe — every 5ft.
For 28mm. diameter pipe — every 6ft.

MICROBORE PIPES IN JOISTS

Microbore pipes can be fitted through joists exactly as for small bore ones. Alternatively, the joist can be drilled about halfway up, as for an electric cable. The hole should be about ½in. larger than the diameter of the pipe, with the resulting space filled with a flexible material.

PASSING PIPES THROUGH WALLS AND CEILINGS

Where heating pipes need to pass through walls, the pipe should ideally be protected by an outer sleeve, as shown in Fig. 72.

The sleeve is often made from a short length of pipe of the next size up, alternatively plastic tube will suffice. It should be positioned such that there is an air gap all around between it and the heating pipe.

In the case of pipes passing through ceilings, a neater method is often required. It is not advisable to simply

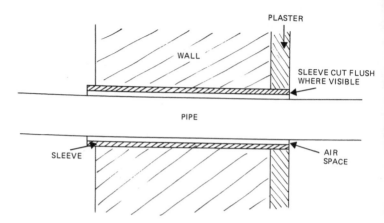

Fig. 72   Protection of a heating pipe, where it passes through a wall.

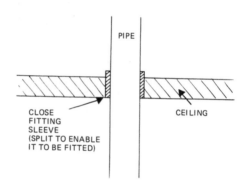

Fig. 73   A heating pipe passing through a ceiling.

plaster the pipe in, since movement will cause the plaster to fall out again, and become unsightly.

A close-fitting plastic sleeve can be used, as shown in Fig. 73. This is plastered neatly into the ceiling, and after decorating, is invisible. The pipe is still able to slide up and down inside the sleeve.

Where pipes are required to pass through floorboards, special treatment is not usually called for. The hole or slot in the board is cut oversize to allow for pipe movement. This is then hidden by the floor covering or carpet, which in any case, is flexible.

MAKING COMPRESSION JOINTS
(Fig. 38, page 78)

The sequence is as follows.

1. Ensure that the pipe end has not been squashed into an oval shape, and that the outside diameter is undented, and fairly smooth.
2. Ensure that the olive is undamaged. Also check the cone recesses inside the nut and body.
3. Clean all parts. Most leaks are caused by sand or grit being inside the joint when the nut is tightened.
4. Pass the nut over the end of the pipe, and slide the olive into position. Some fittings require the olive to be a certain way round.

   The olive must be a good sliding fit on the outside diameter of the pipe. If this is not so, it is likely that the olive size is incorrect. This could occur, for example, when attempting to use a 22mm. olive on an old piece of ¾in. pipe.
5. Push the pipe, and then the olive into the fitting as far as they will go.
6. Take the nut, and screw it on to the thread of the fitting. Tighten by hand as far as possible, and complete by using a wrench or spanner. There is no positive stop on the thread, and the tightness must be judged. Generally, compression joints on stainless steel pipe need to be tightened more than those on copper pipe. This is because stainless steel pipe is harder than copper, and more pressure is required to make the olive bite into the surface.

Provided that all parts are clean and undamaged, a watertight joint can be made without using any sealing compound. However, if preferred, a non-toxic compound such as Boss White can be used. This is smeared on to the pipe and olive prior to assembly, but care must be taken to ensure that none enters the pipe or waterway of the fitting.

MAKING CAPILLARY JOINTS —
PRESOLDERED TYPE (Fig. 39, page 80)

These joints are made as follows:

1. Inspect the pipes and fitting to ensure that they are undamaged.
2. Clean the outside diameter of all pipe ends, and the inside of the fitting with fine steel wool. Do not touch the cleaned areas afterwards.
3. With copper pipes, apply flux to all pipe ends and the inside of the fitting. When using stainless steel

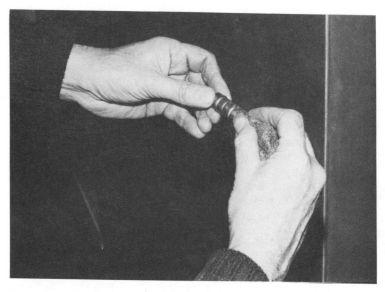

In any type of soldered joint cleanliness is vital. This is achieved by a thorough cleaning with wire wool.

        pipe, a different type of flux is required, and this is applied to each mouth of the fitting only.
4. Insert all pipes into the fitting as far as they will go. Rotate each through a few degrees to distribute the flux.
5. Apply heat to each joint until a complete ring of solder appears. An incomplete ring almost certainly indicates that a joint will leak.
6. Remove surplus flux.

It should be noted that, with any type of capillary joint, all pipes must be soldered into the fitting at the same time. If this is not observed, the heat applied to make the second joint will melt the solder in the first.

The heat is usually applied with a blowlamp. Modern butane gas types are most convenient, since they can be lit far more easily than with paraffin models. It is often necessary to protect the surrounding area from the heat and flames.

MAKING CAPILLARY JOINTS — NON-PRESOLDERED TYPE (Fig. 40, page 80)

Proceed as follows:
1. Inspect the pipes and fitting to ensure that they are undamaged.

When the cleaned and fluxed joint is assembled it is heated evenly using a butane torch until continuous rings of solder form.

2. Clean the outside diameter of all pipe ends, and the inside of the fitting with fine steel wool. Do not touch the cleaned areas afterwards.
3. With copper pipes, apply flux to all pipe ends and the inside of the fitting. When using stainless steel pipe, a different type of flux is required. This is again applied to all pipe ends and the inside of the fitting.
4. Insert all pipes into the fitting as far as they will go. Rotate each through a few degrees to distribute the flux.
5. Apply heat and solder to the first joint. When the solder melts, feed in sufficient to fill the gap between the pipe and fitting. Repeat, in turn, at all other joints on the fitting.

MAKING THREADED JOINTS (Fig. 41, page 81)

Threaded joints are made as follows:

1. Inspect the male and female threads to ensure that they are undamaged. Minor imperfections can be removed with a small file. If in doubt, the joint can be assembled dry to check that the parts will fit.
2. Clean both threads as well as possible.

3. Wind three or four turns of ptfe tape around the male thread. The direction of winding should be such that the tape is caused to wind tighter when the parts are screwed together.
4. Assemble the parts, and tighten with a wrench or spanner.

The ptfe tape gives a quick, clean and convenient method of sealing threaded joints. The traditional method using hemp and Boss White offers none of these advantages, but its sealing properties are somewhat better, especially on large threads.

A more basic way of cutting pipe is in a bench vice with a hacksaw — keep the blade square!

The cut end can be smoothed off with a few strokes of a file.

A half-round file will quickly remove the burr around the cut edge.

16
INSTALLING THE HEATING SYSTEM

In most homes, it will be desirable to install the heating system with as little upheaval as possible. This can be brought about only by careful planning. A suggested sequence of events is laid out below, but this, of course, can be altered.

POSITION THE HEATING UNITS

The heating units are fitted into position. It is important to ensure that holes for wall plugs are not drilled oversize. This is especially important when using fibre or wooden plugs, as these sometimes shrink due to the effect of heat. Radiators, when full of water, can weigh a considerable amount.

At this stage, control, lockshield and air bleed valves can be fitted, together with any blanking plugs required.

FIT THE HEADER TANK FOR THE DOMESTIC WATER

If a new header tank for the domestic water is required, this can now be fitted. Any existing hot water system must be put out of action at this stage.

Most central heating systems require a feed and expansion tank, and this is usually installed adjacent to the header tank for the domestic water. This second tank can be fitted now, in which case some provision must be made to prevent it being filled with water.

FIT THE INDIRECT HOT WATER CYLINDER

An existing hot water cylinder can now be replaced with an indirect type, if this is required.

The cold feed from the header tank, and the hot supply to the taps must be connected. For cylinders which are not self-priming, the two connections carrying the primary water to and from the boiler need not be made. This arrangement enables the domestic hot water system to be brought back into operation, using an electric immersion heater.

For self-priming cylinders, the two primary connections must be capped if the domestic hot water system is required to operate.

INSTALL THE BOILER AND FLUE

Where boilers are fitted into confined spaces, it is sometimes necessary to complete a certain amount of pipework at this stage.

Manufacturers' instructions must be faithfully observed if safety and best performance are to be achieved.

Most boilers include a tapping for a safety valve, which should be fitted. If no tapping is available, a position in the pipework, near to the boiler, should be chosen.

MAKE A PIPE TO REPLACE THE PUMP

A short length of pipe should be prepared, with a fitting at each end. The fittings must be identical to those on the pump, and the same distance apart. The pipe is fitted into the system instead of the pump during flushing.

COMPLETE THE PIPEWORK

All pipework should now be completed, and the pump replacement pipe fitted instead of the pump. Mechanical and electrical control valves need to be included, but not wired. If possible, leave all joints accessible until after the system is filled.

FILL WITH WATER

The system is now almost ready to fill with water, but first:

1. Check the complete installation, to ensure that no connections have been missed.
2. Fully open all control and lockshield valves where possible. Electrical valves usually have provision for this, but some mechanical ones do not.
3. Close all air bleed valves.

As the system fills, all of the air which was inside needs to be bled off. This is achieved by opening each air bleed valve in turn, starting with the lowest.

CHECK FOR LEAKS AND CORRECT IF NECESSARY

With the system full of water, and with as much air as possible having been removed, check for leaks. These will, of course, appear at joints, and can be corrected as follows:

1. Compression joints — tighten the nut further. If this fails to stop the leak, the system must be drained. The defective joint is then dismantled and reassembled using a non-toxic sealing compound such as Boss White. In extreme cases, the olive, or even the fitting itself, will need to be replaced.
2. Capillary joints — the system must be drained, and the area dried out as much as possible. The fitting is

then reheated and resoldered. Some heating engineers will not attempt to resolder existing fittings. They simply replace the defective part with a new one.

As stated above, it is important to dry the inside and outside of the pipework near to the site of the leak before attempting to resolder. This is because a good joint cannot be obtained if water or steam are present. It is usually possible to dry the inside of a pipe by warming it with a blowlamp.

3. Threaded joints — the system must be drained and the joint remade using new ptfe tape, or hemp and Boss White.

FLUSH THE SYSTEM

Attach a hose to the drain fitting, and open the valve. This will allow water to run continuously through the system. During this time, the amount of water which is run off is replaced from the feed and expansion tank. Flushing in this manner should be allowed to continue for about 15 minutes.

FIT THE PUMP

Close the valve at each side of the pump position, and remove the replacement pipe. Flush the pump through with tap water, and fit into position. Open the valves on each side, and remove air from the pump by opening the bleed valve.

FIT INSULATION

Fit insulation where necessary. Places where this is generally required are:

1. Around header, feed and expansion tanks, where they are sited in an attic.
2. Around pipework, where it runs through an unheated space.
3. Around heating pipework, where it is desirable to reduce heat emission.
4. Around the hot water cylinder.

REPLACE PIPE COVERING

Replace floorboards or pipe boxes where necessary. These should be secured with screws to give easy access in the future.

The heating system is now ready to operate. It must, however, be left in this condition until the electrical installation is complete.

17
ELECTRICAL INSTALLATION

There is no particular order in which the installation of the electrical equipment needs to be carried out. This chapter is therefore devoted to giving a number of notes which, it is hoped, will be found useful.

Items of central heating control equipment are supplied with detailed instruction leaflets. These must always be followed and should be kept for future reference.

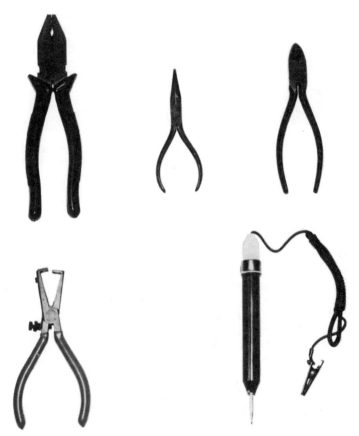

A useful selection of electrical handtools. Top to bottom, left to right: electrician's pliers, wiring pliers, diagonal cutters, wire-stripping tool, continuity tester.

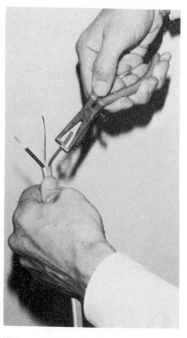 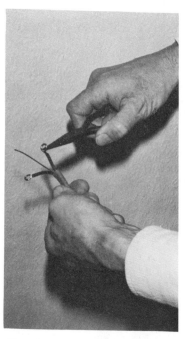

Wire-strippers enable the insulation to be removed without risk of damage to the conductors.

The wiring pliers are used to form neat loops for connection to screw terminals.

MAINS SUPPLY

Where a ring circuit is available, the supply for the central heating circuit can be taken directly from the ring. Failing this, a special supply cable will have to be run from a vacant fuseway on the distribution board or consumer unit. The supply must include an earth connection so that earthing of items of equipment may be carried out in accordance with the maker's recommendations.

FUSED ISOLATOR

Some means of isolating the electrical circuit must be provided, and a fused isolator is most convenient for this. It is very important to fit an isolator into circuits containing motorized valves, as some of these have live parts even when the heating system is switched off at the time-switch or programmer. The isolator used must be of the *double-pole type*.

TIME-SWITCH/PROGRAMMER

The time-switch or programmer is the item which is most often reset, and it should be sited conveniently.

RELAYS

It is most likely that relays will need to be either enclosed in a protective box, or sited out of reach. This is because they contain a number of electrically live parts which are difficult to cover. Most relays are designed to be mounted on a vertical surface.

HOT WATER CYLINDER THERMOSTAT

This thermostat is strapped to the outside of the cylinder, using a band which passes around the circumference. The unit itself must not be covered with heat insulation.

Heat resisting cable is required because the thermostat reaches almost the same temperature as the domestic hot water.

ROOM THERMOSTAT

The room thermostat should be fixed in a position which is representative of the space being controlled. Many installers choose the hall. This is, in fact, a most unsuitable place, because:

1. Each time that the outside door is opened, the hall cools rapidly. This causes the heating to be switched on when the rest of the building may already be at the required temperature.
2. The hall is not a living space, and nobody spends much time there.

The thermostat should not be sited where there is any source of heat other than from the heating system. For systems which contain radiators and fan-convectors, the room thermostat controlling the radiators should not be sited in the same room as a fan-convector.

CONTROL VALVES

Control valves must never be installed with any electrical parts below the level of the pipework. This is to avoid additional problems in the event of a leak. The electrical parts must not be covered with heat insulation.

FAN-CONVECTORS

Fan-convectors require their own power supply to operate the fan. This can be taken from a convenient 13 amp wall socket, or a special supply can be provided.

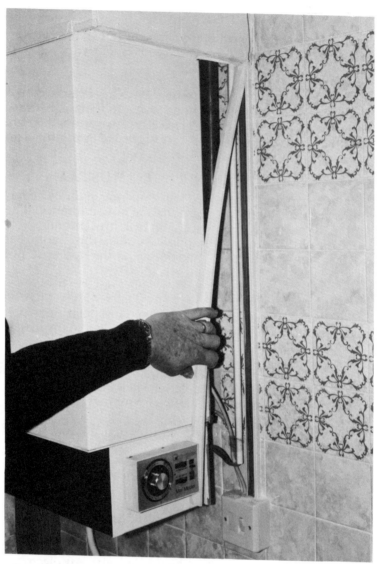

This already neat kitchen corner installation is made neater and safer by the use of plastic trunking.

WIRING

In all parts of the circuit where high temperatures will not be encountered, pvc insulated cables can be used. These should be of the single-strand type and of 1.5 sq.mm. size.

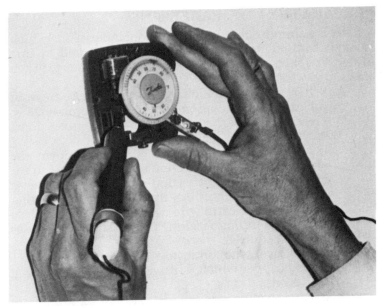

A continuity tester can be used to confirm thermostat contact operation, as well as for general wiring continuity checks.

Heat resisting cables are required where temperatures are high. Such areas would be inside the boiler casework, and at the hot water cylinder thermostat, pump and control valves. Some of these items are sold complete with a short length of suitable cable.

All cables should be adequately supported by plastic clips or some other suitable method.

Where a cable is required to pass through a hole in a sheet metal panel, such as a boiler casing, a rubber grommet must be fitted. This will ensure that the cable insulation cannot chafe on any sharp edges around the hole.

SAFETY

Electrical wiring between the various items of control equipment and to the supply represents a potential hazard if badly carried out. Therefore, in the interests of producing an installation which is both *neat* and *safe* a little space will now be devoted to some of the basic techniques of electrical wiring. Some simple testing techniques will also be included.

PREPARATION OF CABLE ENDS

This is a simple enough task but, nonetheless, one which is often badly done if the number of badly fitted 13 amp plugs to be seen is any indication! The main points to watch are as follows:

1. When stripping the outer sheath take care to avoid nicking the insulation on individual conductors. Here is an easy method often used by professional electricians.

   Using the diagonal cutters just cut down the sheath at the cable end enough to gain access to the earth conductor. Then gripping this earth wire with the pliers, and holding the cable with the other hand, pull the earth wire back against the sheath so that it cuts through it along the length of the cable as far as is required.

2. When baring the conductors themselves avoid nicks in the copper which will weaken the conductor at that point.

3. Ensure that just enough insulation is removed from conductors so that, while there is sufficient wire to form a loop that will be held securely under a screw head, there is not so much that there is a risk of a short-circuit between adjacent conductors. Fig. 74 illustrates the right and wrong ways of forming cable ends.

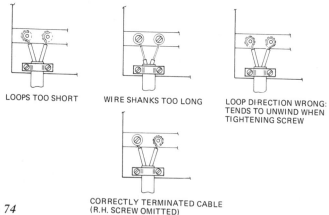

LOOPS TOO SHORT   WIRE SHANKS TOO LONG   LOOP DIRECTION WRONG: TENDS TO UNWIND WHEN TIGHTENING SCREW

Fig. 74   CORRECTLY TERMINATED CABLE (R.H. SCREW OMITTED)

As for the tools themselves — diagonal cutters, about 5ins. in length, will be found very useful. A good alter-

A neat amateur installation of timer and over-ride switch in the corner of a larder.

For the outside boiler house the inclusion of a FROST-STAT is money well spent.

135

native is a pair of electrician's side-cutting pliers. Either of these will cut wire and cable to length and strip insulation but each has its own particular limitations. A craft knife will often be found useful in cable stripping if due care is observed. A rather more fool-proof way of baring conductors is to use wire-strippers. These have the advantage that, when correctly set, they will remove insulation without either effort or danger of cutting into the conductor.

SECURITY OF CABLES

The method of securing and protecting a cable depends upon such factors as the route over which the cable must pass (e.g. under floor, in or over walls, etc.), the purpose of the cable and possibly the construction of the dwelling.

To take an example of each, consider first the routing of the cable connecting the room thermostat with a boiler installation in a kitchen.

With a suspended floor the route may be as follows:

1. Drop down kitchen wall to under-floor level.
2. Pass between joists or through *small* cut-outs in joists to living room.
3. Rise up living room wall to required site for thermostat.

The under-floor section poses no problem apart from the lifting of some floorboards to facilitate passage of the cable.

The section of the cable in the kitchen may have to be surface-mounted if the wall is tiled since it may not be thought desirable to remove tiles merely in order to hide a few feet of cable. In any case part of the cable may be hidden by the installation itself or a kitchen cupboard. Even so it is best not to be tempted to let the cable hang free but to secure it in the best way possible. Plastic clips are not really applicable to tiled walls unless one can drive the pins through the grouting into the plaster beneath. A very neat and absolutely safe alternative is to pass the cable (perhaps with other cable as well) through a length of plastic *trunking*. This can be stuck or screwed to the wall, hides the cable completely and presents a really workmanlike finish to the job. This idea is shown in Fig. 75.

We are now faced with the problem of getting the cable up the living room wall to the thermostat.

Assuming that some re-decoration is acceptable the neatest solution is to chisel a narrow channel in the plaster from floor to thermostat height. The cable is laid in this channel, held in place with a few clips, which merely maintain its position while new plaster laid in the channel is

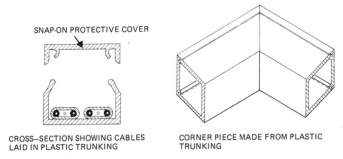

SNAP-ON PROTECTIVE COVER

CROSS—SECTION SHOWING CABLES
LAID IN PLASTIC TRUNKING

CORNER PIECE MADE FROM PLASTIC
TRUNKING

Fig. 75

setting. It is important to remember to leave an adequate length of cable for connection to the thermostat; failure to do so can be very embarassing!

This method of making an invisible connection to the thermostat is not really suitable for lath-and-plaster walls. It becomes necessary then to mount the cable on the surface of the wall. The plastic trunking mentioned previously can be used to advantage here to give a safe, neat job.

Unprotected cables should be avoided at all costs especially in vulnerable positions. Placed in cupboards, nooks and crannies and at all times well secured they can be tolerated. But not on exposed walls.

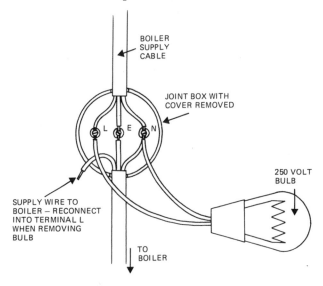

BOILER
SUPPLY
CABLE

JOINT BOX WITH
COVER REMOVED

250 VOLT
BULB

SUPPLY WIRE TO
BOILER – RECONNECT
INTO TERMINAL L
WHEN REMOVING
BULB

TO
BOILER

Fig. 76 Wiring a test bulb, to check the electrical supply to the boiler.

TESTING

When the electrical installation is complete, is can be tested prior to firing the boiler. By adjusting the thermostats to above or below the ambient temperature, the operation of the pump and control valves can be checked.

To check the energizing of the boiler, is may be necessary to connect a 240 volt test bulb across the boiler terminals, as shown in Fig. 76. This will light when the boiler is being supplied with power.

In some circuits using motorized valves, a time delay between switching on, and the boiler and pump being energized will occur. The length of this delay can be up to about one minute.

18
CONNECTION TO THE PUBLIC SUPPLIES

At some point the completed installation has to be connected to the public gas and electricity supplies. Of course, in the case of an oil-fired installation, for example, connection to the gas supply is not relevant. The questions to be asked here concern, not techniques as such, but degrees of responsibility. Is it safe, is it legal for the d-i-y installer to make the final connections to the gas and electricity supplies? Consider each case in turn.

CONNECTION TO THE GAS SUPPLY

The first point to be clear about is that the responsibility for the safe operation of the installation rests with the *installer*. Therefore, although connections to the gas supply *on the outlet side* of the meter are the legal responsibility of the consumer, this does not mean that the d-i-y installer should, willy-nilly, make the connection himself. He may run his pipework from the boiler to a suitable point adjacent to the meter but the final connection should be made by a qualified installer. This is, in fact, the recommendation of the Gas Safety Regulations (1972) and may also be the subject of Building Regulations and local authority requirements. Obviously a fee will be charged for this service but it will be convenient to arrange to have the boiler fired up at the same time and it is reassuring to have a qualified person on site during this phase.

Assuming, therefore, that a qualified person is to make the final connection, it is useful to consider just how to run the pipework that is to connect the boiler to the meter. Assuming that a gas supply to the building exists and that there is at least one gas appliance in use (for example a gas cooker), the general principle to be observed is that the new pipe to the boiler should be connected as close to the meter as practicable. It may be tempting to connect into a cooker supply if there is one nearby. This is a temptation that is best resisted unless one is sure that the outlet pipe is of adequate diameter (see Fig. 77).

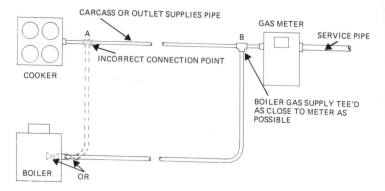

Fig. 77 Layout of gas supply pipes showing correct and incorrect tee points.

If the boiler supply is taken from the cooker supply at point A, then the length of the supply pipe between A and the meter will be common to both boiler and cooker. If the cooker has one or more pilot lights then the sudden flow of a large volume of gas through the outlet supply pipe, when the boiler ignites, may cause a pressure drop sufficient to extinguish the pilot light(s). This potentially hazardous situation is entirely avoided by supplying the boiler from a tee-junction at point B.

The installation recommendations should be followed with regard to the diameter of pipe used but it will probably be 22mm., possibly reducing to 15mm. at the boiler.

CONNECTION TO THE ELECTRICITY SUPPLY

The situation here is a little more straightforward although, as in the case of gas, responsibility rests with the installer for work carried out on the consumer side of the meter. The additional load imposed by gas, oil or solid-fuel central heating on the electricity supply is minimal but, nonetheless, if the consumer unit is used to supply this power, the local electricity board will need to be informed. A form for this purpose is obtainable from the local electricity showroom. As a result a call will be made by an inspector of the board but this will merely verify that the connection made is to the satisfaction of the board. He will not carry out an inspection of the installer's wiring in detail.

If the power is taken from a 13 amp socket on the ring circuit then the installation merely becomes another plug-in appliance and inspection is not necessary.

This leaves one further aspect to consider. The d-i-y installer, may wish to receive a vote of confidence in his electrical wiring. The best way to get this is to contact a reputable and qualified electrician and pay him a fee to inspect the work. It is reassuring to know that an expert has passed one's work.

In case of uncertainties the following authorities should be consulted:

Building Regulations

Local authority requirements

Local Water Board

I.E.E. wiring regulations — Institution of Electrical
Engineers,
Savoy Place,
LONDON, WC2R 0BL

The Gas Safety Regulations (1972)

BS.5376 Pt.2, BS.5440 Pt.2,

BS.5449 Pt.1, and CP.331 Pts.2 and 3
British Standards Institution,
2, Park Street,
LONDON, W1A 2BS
Sales Dept.,
Newton House,
101, Pentonville Road,
LONDON, N1 9ND.

19
COMMISSIONING

Assuming that the pipework system and electrical control circuit have been completed, the installation is almost ready to start up. First, the various thermostats, where fitted, should be set.

1. Boiler thermostat to 180°F.
2. Domestic water temperature thermostat to 130°F.
3. Room thermostat to 60°F, 65°F or 70°F, depending on the required temperature of the room in which it is sited.
4. Mechanical radiator thermostats fully open.
5. Check also that all lockshield valves on the heating units are fully open.

The pump should be set in accordance with the calculations shown in Chapter 9 (page 70). If these calculations have not been carried out, a low setting should be selected at first.

FIRING THE BOILER

This should be carried out as follows:

1. Solid fuel. Firing simply consists of lighting the fire, and regulating in accordance with the instructions issued by the manufacturer.
2. Oil. Most oil companies offer a commissioning service, and it is advisable to take advantage of this. With these boilers, the air/oil mixture must be set correctly if best operation is to be achieved. Special equipment is necessary in order to make the setting.
3. Gas. Again, the gas board will commission the boiler for a small fee. Setting of these boilers is much more simple than with oil models, and usually consists of adjusting the gas pressure, and checking the injectors.

STARTING THE HEATING SYSTEM

When the boiler is running, the central heating system can be started up by energizing the pump, or opening valves as required. As the water in the system is heated, oxygen is given off. This is removed by opening the air bleed valves in turn.

In order to remove all of the oxygen, balancing of the system should not be attempted for at least one week. All air bleed valves, however, should be checked each day, and any oxygen allowed to escape.

Always switch the pump off before opening any air bleed valve.

Sealed, high temperature systems should first be run at normal temperature and pressure, and increased when the installation has been found to be satisfactory.

BALANCING THE SYSTEM

It was shown in Chapter 9 (page 69), that each part of the heating system offers a different resistance to the water flow. Most water will pass through that part of the system which offers least resistance. Without balancing, the heating units on this part of the system will reach the highest temperature, and will thus emit most heat.

The object of balancing is to adjust the resistance offered by each part of the system, so that they become equal. The flow of water will thus be equally shared.

For correct balancing, a pair of clip-on pipe thermometers are required. As the name suggests, these are small thermometers which can be clipped on to a pipe. They indicate the temperature of the pipe and, almost, the temperature of the water inside.

Correctly, balancing should be carried out when the outside temperature is at the designed level, that is 30°F. In fact, a fairly good compromise can be reached at any time, leaving final small adjustments to be made when the outside temperature is suitable.

The operation is carried out as follows:
1. Open all control and lockshield valves fully. Open all bleed valves in turn to remove oxygen. Allow the system to reach operating temperature.

    In the case of high temperature systems, move on to 4.
2. Place a hand on each heating unit in turn, to estimate the temperature. Partially close the lockshield valves on the hottest heating units. Leave the system for about one hour for the temperatures to stabilize.
3. Repeat 2, until each heating unit feels to be at about the same temperature.
4. Choose one heating unit, and clip one thermometer to the flow pipe. Clip the second thermometer to the return pipe, and leave for a few minutes for the readings to settle. Note the difference between the two readings.

5. Repeat 4, for all heating units.
6. Adjust the lockshield valves, until the difference between the two readings is the same for all heating units.

The system is now balanced. If the difference between the readings for each heating unit is 20°F, the pump setting is correct. If the difference is less than 20°F, the pump setting must be increased.

The difference between the readings is, in fact, the designed temperature drop for the system. For microbore systems designed for a 30°F or 40°F temperature drop, this increased figure should be reflected in the thermometer readings.

CORROSION

From the moment that water enters the heating system, corrosion begins. There are two main reasons for this:

1. Mains water contains a certain amount of dissolved oxygen. This is eventually driven out of the water, and removed through a bleed valve. Before this can happen, however, a small amount of red rust is formed on steel surfaces, such as the inside of radiators. Any water entering the system from the feed and expansion tank carries fresh supplies of oxygen.
2. When two dissimilar metals are in contact with each other, and in water, a minute electric current passes between them. This causes corrosion.

   In a heating system, there are several different metals. The resulting corrosion causes far more damage than the oxygen in 1.

The rate of corrosion can be greatly reduced, but not completely eliminated, by the use of an inhibitor. Several varieties are available, and each is used in accordance with the instructions issued by the manufacturer. The system had to be drained, and the inhibitor added to the feed and expansion tank. Air removal through the bleed valves will again be required, but the balance of the system should not be affected.

Corrosion inhibitor cannot be used in systems with self-priming hot water cylinders.

INSTRUCTION SHEETS

Most items of central heating equipment, including controls, are supplied with detailed instruction and installation sheets. These should be kept, as they could prove to be invaluable in the event of further work or modification being required.